Since Concern was founded in 1968 our aim has been to improve the lives of the poorest people on the planet. People who go to bed hungry each night, people with little access to safe water, healthcare or schooling and people who in times of crises or natural disaster are most at risk of losing the few possessions they own.

Today Concern Worldwide is one of the world's most respected international NGOs, working with over 300 partners in 25 countries throughout the developing world. We listen to the very poorest people, they know more about poverty, disease and discrimination than anyone else and armed with that knowledge we under-take long term development work and respond to emergency situations as they arise.

We place immense importance on working with individuals, communities and local government's and we empower people to develop the best and most sustainable solutions that work for them.

In the face of unacceptable poverty and the denial of basic human rights our campaign and advocacy work brings our experience to the highest levels of decision and policy making. We aim to give the poorest of the poor a voice, knowing that justice on a global level demands that they be heard and respected.

DISPATCHES FROM THE DEVELOPING WORLD

The Concern Worldwide 2011 Writing Competition

Edited by
Michael Doorly

The Liffey Press

Published by
The Liffey Press
Ashbrook House, 10 Main Street
Raheny, Dublin 5, Ireland
www.theliffeypress.com

A catalogue record of this book is
available from the British Library.

ISBN 978-1-908308-13-9

Illustrations by Conor Gallagher.

Printed in Ireland by Gemini International.

Contents

Part 1
JUNIOR CATEGORY
(12–15 years old)

Contents

Contents

Part 2
SENIOR CATEGORY
(16–18 years old)

Part 3
COLLEGE STUDENTS
(full or part-time)

Part 4
ADULT CATEGORY
(over 19 years old)

Foreword

Tom Arnold
Chief Executive, Concern Worldwide

It's the territory of cliché to talk about how things have changed so much in the world, in so many areas of our lives over the last 20, 30, 40, 50 years. It is close to impossible today to imagine what the world was like back some few years ago.

For most of the 800 people who entered this year's Concern Creative Writing Competition a mobile telephone is a given. Even in the remotest parts of the world there is telephone coverage. The world is no longer agog with instant communication.

This year's writing competition asked entrants to think of themselves as journalists stationed in a developing world country working for an internationally renowned newspaper. It's their job to file copy about life in their adopted home.

A journalist is a wordsmith, who reports on what's happening. They tell the news. A journalist is someone who crafts words in such a way that he or she tempts the reader to keep reading. It is a sine qua non that a journalist tells the truth.

Once a word, a sentence, a sentiment is 'out there' it can never be taken back. And in the world of instant communication, there is a feeding frenzy to parse and analyse every word that is said, especially, the words of those who are in the spotlight. And for that reason, public personages normally employ speech writers and advisers to guide them in what they say, the words they use.

The words we use are important. They give us the power to communicate our story. In the days before our current 'technological revolution' we said that a picture was worth a thousand words.

Photoshop has forced us to look more closely. It's easy to doctor pictures. But it also can be easy to doctor words and tell untruths.

A journalist, a newspaper, all media outlets have a privilege but a terrible responsibility always to tell the truth. A journalist's job is unique and challenging.

The essays in this book are fiction. But the writers aspire to tell the story as they see it. And that surely must fill us with hope and a belief that people, wherever they live, are really excited and interested in telling the truth.

As recently as the 1950s journalists were under pressure as to how they would get their copy back to the office in time for the next day's newspaper. Today, instant communication is a given.

In spite of all the advances in communication, telling the simple truth can still be a complex matter.

The Concern Writing Competition gives people an opportunity to use words in a creative and constructive manner. It is yet another vehicle Concern uses to put the spotlight on the developing world. With one billion people without enough food to eat we need every tool at our disposal to explain the reality.

Words are hugely important, words that are true and make sense. The writings in this book clearly show that people, whoever they are, wherever they live, are always interested in discovering what's real and telling others about it. Congratulations to all who entered this year's competition.

Preface

Michael Doorly

Every day here in Concern we receive constant reminders of the goodness and generosity of people. From those offering to volunteer in 'some small way' at an event or around the office to those who go to extraordinary lengths to donate or campaign on behalf of the world's poorest people. Entering the annual Concern Writing Competition falls somewhere in between these two, but despite the time, effort and skill involved it is still very much an act of generosity.

In this, the fourth annual Concern Creative Writing Competition, we challenged entrants to imagine themselves a journalist stationed in a 'developing world' country working for an internationally renowned newspaper and being asked (told!) by their editor to write a 1,000 word article on one of the following topics: Living on less than $2 a day; Imagining the future of a child born today in the developing world; or Lessons we can learn from the developing world. As in the previous three years of the competition we were delighted to receive hundreds of entries from 37 countries around the world.

That so many entered the spirit of the competition made for sometimes humorous but always interesting and engaging reading, with one young contributor writing, 'Perhaps it's just the cynicism of my profession that I couldn't help but dwell on a scenario that is both bleak and dark.' It is interesting to note that of the three possible topics the one least favoured (*overwhelmingly*) by our entrants was that of 'Lessons we can learn from the developing world', which in itself is a lesson about how we in the so called 'developed' world still need to listen and learn from those who live in the midst of extreme poverty and hardship.

Hosting the Concern Creative Writing Competition relies on the generosity and goodwill of not just the entrants but an army of first and second round judges, who read each of the 800 'articles' not just once but twice, and so we would like to express our sincere thanks to them and of course to our four final round judges, Mick Clifford (*Irish Examiner* and *Sunday Times*), Lara Marlowe (*The Irish Times*), Catherine Hallaran (*Irish Daily Star*) and Patricia Harty (*Irish America* magazine).

We are delighted to present to you in this book the 'full article' from our winning and short listed entries across each of the four competition categories, along with over a hundred noteworthy 'passages' from other entrants. We hope that you not only read and enjoy them but that their words will inspire you to work toward a more just and fair world for all.

Michael Doorly is Head of Active Citizenship in Concern

A Word from Our Judges . . .

Mick Clifford
Irish Examiner and Sunday Times

'Comfort the afflicted, and afflict the comfortable.' The dictum is a long standing one in journalism, although its origin is unclear. It says all that needs to be said about one of the primary duties of a journalist – to shine a light into dark corners, particularly when some force of darkness would prefer to deflect the light.

Reading the entries to the Concern Creative Writing Competition, I was struck time and again by the manner in which the entrants were shining a light into dark corners. The task set for the entrants was to imagine that they are a journalist, stationed in a developing country, writing for an internationally renowned newspaper. The standard of the work was such that I often forgot that these writers were imagining themselves as journalists. Many would quite easily pass for the real thing, such was the manner in which they went about the task.

Bringing to life the everyday struggles of people who live in some of the poorest parts of the world qualifies under the line, 'comfort the afflicted'. The comfort being offered is merely to tell the story of what it is like to live under those conditions. Undertaking this duty to shine a light into a corner of the world where fate has shown its harshest face compels the wider world to look, learn and hopefully address its responsibilities to act in the name of humanity. Therein, the comfortable are afflicted by the reality of the world in which they live.

Shining the light is one thing, but if it isn't done in a manner that makes readers sit up and take notice it can end up redundant. Here, also, the quality of the entrants was staggering. Most of those that I read immediately reached in, grabbed my imagination and took me to a village or rural outpost of Africa to spend time with its residents. The world created on the page of so many entrants was real, and no more can be asked of any writer.

I sincerely hope that all of those who entered this competition continue to write in one form or another. There was a lot of light shining off the page, and it is a precious resource.

Lara Marlowe

Washington Correspondent, The Irish Times

In judging the Concern essays, I looked for original imagery and language, and the ability to tell a story. Most of the contestants chose the theme I would have chosen myself – imagining the future of a child born today. The best brought you into the life of a specific child and made you feel you knew him or her, often starting with the infant's birth.

In one of my favourite essays, from the 12-15 year-old Junior category, children lie awake in a shanty in Malawi, listening to their mother's screams as Bwerani is born. Bwerani, I learned, means 'you are welcome'. Sensory details brought a lot to this essay: morning light, winter cold piercing the children's thin clothes, gnawing hunger, the image of Bwerani pouncing on mice. Several of the essays talked about parents in developing countries wanting education for their children, but this one showed you how poverty and hard labour destroyed Bwerani's will to learn to read and write, and led to his early death.

Another essay from the same age group, about a newborn named Sana in Tunisia, reminded one that the lives of girls are particularly hard in the developing world. It deftly wove the events of this year's 'Arab Spring' into the child's story, as a source of hope for the future.

In the 16-18 year-old category, a similar story hailed the birth of a daughter called Sasmita ('smiling') to the Kumar family in Calcutta. Again, it was the imagery and details that made the story so effective: the absence of a doctor to deliver the baby, the description of clay, wattle, timber and galvanised steel huts, the local rat-infested dump where Sasmita's brother Hassan collects old batteries, rags and metal.

In the same category, the essay about an infant born in Haiti on the anniversary of the 2010 earthquake, which I had reported on for *The Irish Times*, was accurate and effective.

The two best essays in the college student category had to overcome a major failing to win my favour: neither contained a single paragraph break! But I was won over by the detailed description of the ravages of the Lord's Resistance Army in Uganda in one, and the complete picture of childhood in India conveyed by the other.

Younger contestants had more imagination and were better story-tellers, while older contestants tended to pack their more general essays with telling facts and figures. A notable exception to this was a newspaper-style story for *The Manila Bulletin* in the adult category which imagined the life of a middle-aged Filipino called Phil who earns less than $2.00 a day collecting garbage.

This was an impressive collection of essays. The quality was so high that it was painstaking work to judge among them.

Catherine Hallaran

Political Correspondent, Irish Daily Star

In an age when society in general is so consumed with reality TV and entertainment, it is refreshing to see so many people with an interest in helping others. The Concern Writing competition brought home to me that there is more to life than 'looking after number one', even in a tough economic climate.

People understand that there are millions around the world far worse off than them, millions who are living in such abject poverty that food is a luxury and not a necessity and millions who have to trek for days just to get basic medical attention.

The attention to detail in the essays – across all categories – was incredible. The reader was brought immediately to the scene of the story and could feel the desperation of many of the people who were written about. But there were also the moving and heart-lifting stories about how a little bit of kindness can go so far to help people not only survive, but to move forward with their lives so they in turn can help others.

In today's world, where so many people are being impacted directly by the global recession, Concern has shown that there are people out there who care and will – without a second thought – go that extra mile to help.

It is very easy to get distracted in the modern world but there is another side to every story. While the lucky few may be living it up in luxury, there are millions who scrape by on an hour-to-hour basis. We cannot allow these people to be forgotten. Their voices need to be heard and they need our help. These essays have given us a snapshot of their lives, their troubles, their hopes and their dreams.

Whether help comes in the form of a small financial donation or the work being done on a voluntary basis by thousands of people around the globe, it does make a difference.

And the essays submitted to this competition will also make a difference – by opening the eyes of millions to the plight of those most in need of help.

Congratulations to all involved.

Patricia Harty

Editor/Co-Founder, Irish America magazine

The essays in this book are finely crafted and open a window onto the developing world through which once you look it will be hard to turn away. Can I ever look at my closet full of shoes again and not see that child working on a dump who dreams of a pair of sandals 'so that when I step on something sharp, my feet won't get hurt', or not see those two young sisters and their grandmother who share one pair of communal flip flops? Apart from stopping me from whining about my own life, this book infused me with a new commitment to Concern. Whether it's helping women through small loans to start their own income-generating projects, or supporting drop-in centres in Quetta, Pakistan, where young 'garbage pickers' have a chance to rest, play and learn, these essays show that even in the direst of circumstances where there's Concern, there's hope.

Part One

JUNIOR CATEGORY

(12–15 years old)

FIRST PLACE – JUNIOR

Gavin Tucker

*Lanesboro Community College,
County Longford, Ireland, Age 15*

**THE FUTURE OF A CHILD BORN
TODAY IN THE DEVELOPING WORLD**

Nesrine is curled up on the floor of her dark hut, the freezing sweat pouring down her face, her ivory-white teeth clenched together with the unbearable pain coursing through her. She reaches for the table-top, trying to get up from her pitiful position but she falls, defeated. She knows her child is arriving. She screams, scared and all alone.

After an excruciating three hours, the child is born. She smiles at it, holding it lovingly as if to protect it from its future. It will live hungry and impoverished, and die lonely and abused. She looks and sees it is a girl and cries for her. She will never go to school, will never have a job, she will be the prey of lustful men. She was destined for this fate the moment she was conceived. Nesrine calls her Sana because she is beautiful for now.

Sana is Nesrine's thirteenth birthday present.

Sana is born into the Tunisia of 2010, a time when the African continent, crippled by the restraints of its dictators and poverty, is lifting its eyes up from the darkness of its past to face into the light of cultural, social and economic revolution. But the inhabitants of this glorious, beautiful country still bear the deep scars from the chains of its corrupt, hungry and poor past. What has shaped the Tunisia of Sana's ancestors? What kind of Tunisia has she has been dragged into? What changes will she encounter on her journey through the Tunisian sands of tomorrow?

The Africa we read of in the history books was steeped in corruption and exploitation, colonised by the Spanish and the British, dominated by the whites. Africans were shipped off to the New World by the thousands to face further injustice, or remain as slaves in their own lands. But there came a stage when the people of Africa had the courage and bravery to say 'enough', they stood up for independence and democracy, the right to be the masters of their own realm. Colonies were inspired by each other as a movement of independence spread across the entire continent. After many years of toil and struggle, the kingdoms of Europe were driven out. But as the Africans would find, as well as cruel Europeans, there exist cruel Africans also.

However, those early champions of independence, Charles Taylor, Muammar Gaddafi and Robert Mugabe, eventually became synonymous with corruption and injustice, and the long-awaited dream of fair democracy was still that, a dream. These 'presidents for life' occupied their grandiose and extravagant palaces, enjoying the spoils and riches they stole from their own treasuries whilst being driven about in their fleets of Mercedes, their subjects still too poor to buy shoes.

When I look out the window of my apartment in Tunis, I see children who have spent their formative years accustomed to hopelessness and poverty. They have seen their families scavenging food from rotten carcasses and moulding scrap bins. They have seen the parents they rely on to provide for them begging in the streets. And this is the only life they have ever known.

But today, turn on any news channel or tune to any radio station and listen to the stories of the uprisings in Tunisia, Libya and Egypt. Just as once they stood up against the Europeans, they now stand up against their 'leaders'. The presidential Mercedes has broken down and is burnt out, the president for life skulks in the back alleys, his palace is wrecked and looted, the streets are a melting pot of colour. Pictures of the deposed dictator hang from the balconies defaced and burned. The masses are roaring deafening cheers and hoorahs after having tasted a drop of the soul-enriching elixir of freedom. The people are dancing ecstatically and untiringly in the street – their day has come. The vibrance and colour of a free people explodes from the monotone, sepia brick buildings. But it will be many years before the sooty, dirty fumes from the presidential car leave the Tunisian skies, but Nesrine looks at her daughter and sees the shining light of hope.

For Sana and the children of her age, the winds of revolution are sweeping through the North African air, granting her generation an optimism that was vehemently denied to their families before them. An optimism that their countries will have learned from their bloody pasts, an optimism that will see Sana become literate, sleep in peace at night-time, eventually attend university and ultimately become respected as the equal of a man. She will see her country grow to become a player in the global market, which will free Tunisia from its physical and economic starvation. This victory will not come easy; there will be much resistance to change; there will be much blood spilled; there will be controversy. There will again be corrupt individuals taking advantage of their power, yet today, the future of Africa has never looked better.

The key to unlocking the door to the bright future is finding leaders who have a genuine unconditional love for their country and who will uplift their people, who will take every step possible to promote democracy and economic growth, who will accept serious reform to their country, promoting foreign investment and productivity. This is how Africa will leave poverty behind in the sand dunes. These people will be found in Sana's generation, untainted by the corrupt bureaucracies and dictatorships of the past. These children of the new Africa will shape their own futures.

Sana is one year old now, and a lot has changed in that year. Nesrine's despair has turned to joy as she sees the men and women of her town celebrating in the streets. The wrongs that were done to her and her people can never be righted, and she knows that she herself will probably not live long enough to see her country become great, but she cries with joy for her daughter, Sana. She has, after all, been born into the light.

SECOND PLACE – JUNIOR

Sarah Mighell

Westport Academy of the Arts,
Desert Hot Springs, California, USA,
Age 14

THE FUTURE OF A CHILD BORN
TODAY IN THE DEVELOPING WORLD

Malawi, Africa; 6/7/11 – The darkness of the long night finally succumbs to the rippling, intensifying light of the morning sun. Several children huddle in the corner, trying to escape the coldness of winter that seeps through their thin clothes. Throughout the night, they had laid awake, listening to the inescapable screeches of their mother as she gave birth to their newest brother, a screaming bundle of life named Bwerani, translated as 'you are welcome'. Bwerani was introduced to the developing world of Malawi, Africa, on June 6, 2011. He has three siblings – two brothers and a sister – and his parents. They own no land. They all work at least ten hours a day for just a few dollars per day, and they are all excited to show their world to Bwerani.

Bwerani begins his life in a decrepit shanty about four miles away from the tobacco estate that employs his entire family. He will start working there, alongside his older siblings, by about age five or six, depending on the openings. His oldest brother, Kondwani ('Joyful'), has been working there for years – his body is proof of what lies in store for Bwerani. Nicotine poisoning is very common in children like Bwerani's brother, because their skin is in direct contact with the tobacco. The nicotine is absorbed into

their bodies every day, and Kondwani has already begun to experience the symptomatic headaches and cramps. But Bwerani
does not have to worry about that now; he just yawns demurely
and curls his newborn fingers around whatever lies within reach.

At six years old, Bwerani will rise each morning just before the
sun and receive a handful of food, usually a mushy type of cornmeal, called nsima, before toddling behind his siblings on his way
to work. He will be sure to finish each smattering of his breakfast
before reaching the road, because he can be sure that some other
children on their way to work will try and tackle him to the
ground if they see any trace of nourishment on his hand. He will
follow the long braids that sway around his sister's neck and
shoulders, secretly smiling because he will know that he is lucky
to get food, and that it will somehow end up in his stomach every
single morning. This meal will many times constitute every bite
he receives for a day, something his parents worry over endlessly.
They will labor all day and night to give their children that little
bit of food, but Bwerani will not worry about how his food will
appear. He will just think about the look of pride on his father's
face when he brings home a few dollars each week.

A year or two later will find Bwerani working the same job, but
with longer hours and an insignificant pay raise. He and his sister
will periodically go out to the fields surrounding their home to try
and find something extra to give to their family for dinner. On their
best days, an unlucky mouse will meander into their sight, and
mercilessly, Bwerani will pounce upon it; and he will resist the urge
to build a small fire using cornstalk stubble and cook it on the spot.

By this age, he will have started to learn the English alphabet,
and his mother will continue to tell him to repeat each letter to her
before he goes to sleep each night. He will then crawl to his place
next to his brothers and divert his mind from the writhing of his
stomach over his most recent meal, like his mother wringing out
the cleaning rag. And his brother Kondwani will toss beside him,
suffering from ongoing nicotine poisoning. He will force his eyes

shut against the pounding in his skull and try to catch his breath, which will almost seem futile. The fear of enduring similar pain in the future will enter Bwerani's mind, but he will not worry about that then; he will just repeat the English alphabet in his head, over and over, until he finally falls asleep.

As a teenager, Bwerani will work in the same area as his father at the tobacco estate. The sun will beat down on him and he will stop every few minutes to rest his hands on his knees and wipe the sweat out of his eyes. Kondwani will be there as well, and the brothers will struggle to breathe well enough to be productive and not be fired from the estate. The alphabet will no longer be important to Bwerani – his mother never got the chance to learn how to make and write words with it. She had always planned on being able to give her children an education, but obtaining daily food will have become more difficult and time consuming. Bwerani will decide that English will not even matter in his life, since the regional dialect of Chichewa will be the only language anyone uses at work and home. Bwerani will become an adult without knowing how to read or write. But he will not think about that then – he will just concentrate on the sun as it will slide, painstakingly slowly, into the edge of the world, where it will sink into an abyss that Bwerani will chase after as he walks the four miles home.

The average life expectancy for Malawian men is fifty-six, but Bwerani will only live to be nineteen. Nicotine poisoning will take his life, just like it will take Kondwani's. The developing world lacks the enforcement of laws, such as child safety and labor regulations, which eventually leads to devastating results, like the untimely ending of lives. Bwerani's life is very similar to thousands of children in similar positions throughout Malawi. Malawi has begun to transform into a developed country in both its urban and rural areas, although it still has quite a while to go. Hopefully, the world may soon be able to add Malawi as another successful, organized nation to its list of international powers.

THIRD PLACE – JUNIOR

Kyle Talbot

St. Michael's College,
Dublin, Ireland, Age 15

THE FUTURE OF A CHILD BORN
TODAY IN THE DEVELOPING WORLD

Sarah is a four year old girl born In Ireland and living in Dublin. She is looking forward to starting primary school next week and excited about all the friends she will be making. Sarah's parents can't believe their little girl is off to school already. Her mom is wondering what sandwiches will she make for Sarah's first day, her dad is wondering what's the best and quickest way to Sarah's school at twenty to nine in the morning as they both plan on being there to see if she gets on alright before going off to work.

Halfway around the world is a four year old boy named Zuberi (meaning strong). He is looking forward to working with his mother in the fields next week. They are trying to sow seeds for next year's harvest. This year's harvest was very poor, a blight hit the crops, many people died and one of the dead was his twin brother. He didn't know a lot about life but he knew suffering like people twenty times his age couldn't imagine or even begin to comprehend. Zuberi's mother was worrying about what food she could get for her son, she would worry about herself later. Zuberi's father had died of AIDS shortly after Zuberi's birth. His immune system was slowly weakened leaving him an open target for disease and he died of organ failure. It is no surprise that one of the developing industries in the developing world is coffin making.

Back in Ireland Sarah goes to bed early as tomorrow is her first day at school. Sarah's parents are growing more apprehensive as to whether or not Sarah will adapt well to the change. Her mum has made up her mind about Sarah's lunch. She will give her a ham sandwich, orange juice and a small bar of chocolate as a treat. Sarah's dad is going to take the main road down to the school but turn off into an estate by the busy junction and cut through there instead of waiting for ages for the lights to change.

Zuberi is sleeping on the floor tonight and his mother is sleeping on the bed of hay as she has hurt her back stooping over to maintain the crops all day. Zuberi's mother had wished that he would be able to go to school but she could not afford such an expense, he would just have to work in the fields like she has done her whole life. All he has known she thought to herself as she was lying in bed is poverty and hunger. She remembers the time when he asked for more food when he was younger, but what they had just eaten was the last thing they had to eat for another two days before she could get any money from the company she sells the crops to. She feels they are being severely underpaid for the crops she supplies them but she fears if she speaks out she could be given even less than what she is at the moment. However, she counts herself as one of the lucky ones. Other people would die for the chance to be paid what she is being paid, in fact many have.

Sarah's dad was turning into the estate where he could take a shortcut to the school. Her mum was hoping she hadn't forgotten anything, that she had gotten all the books on the booklist the school gave her. Sarah was in the back seat playing with her toy doll, a bit nervous but excited also when the car pulled up into the school car park. Her mom took her by the hand and the two of them walked into the school with Sarah's dad following close behind. They found the class and met all the other parents and their children eager to start school. Sarah's mum and dad left her in the capable hands of the teacher and went out to the car.

Zuberi's mum took him by the hand as they turned the corner into the field. It was a warm day so the crops would need water, this presented a problem as the nearest river was two miles away. Zuberi and his mother started to walk down the path. This path had been travelled by generations before them and will be a path Zuberi will become very familiar with, its twist and turns, hills and steep slopes. Eventually they reached the river. Zuberi filled one of his water pots before filling the other, his mum carried the biggest load with almost half her body weight on her shoulders. They began to slowly walk back to their field. When they arrived they filled smaller containers with water and started watering the roots of the much dehydrated crops. Zuberi was tired and hungry so they took a break and had half an apple that Zuberi's mom got from the market with the little money she had made from tending the crops.

Sarah had finished her first day at school and was in the car with her mom telling her all about the exciting times she had and all the new people she met. She said she sat beside a girl named Lauren and they both played with the Lego blocks. On their way home they had their dinner from McDonald's as a treat for her being such a good girl at school that day. Sarah was thirsty when they got home and she got a glass down from the cabinet with the help of her mom and poured herself a glass of water from the tap.

Zuberi was tired when they got home and he fell asleep straight away as tomorrow when he got up he would have to do it all again. The next morning he woke up to find his mum lying unconscious on the floor. She had died of an undiagnosed heart condition brought about by malnutrition. Zuberi was left all alone. He would have to live life without his mother there to protect him or care for him.

Sarah went on to finish school and go to college. Her parents are very proud of her and hope she will go on to do great things.

Zuberi's future is fraught with hardship and poverty. He will have to face hunger and starvation for the rest of his life. He will travel the path to the river as long as his legs can carry him there and back with his plastic containers of water. He will be paid what his mother was paid for all her hard work. He will sleep where his mother slept after a hard day's work. He will know what his brother knew and he would accept it and get on with it and he will do what his name suggests – he will be strong.

SHORTLIST – JUNIOR

Michael Cronin
Ardscoil Ris, Dublin, Age 15

LIVING ON LESS THAN $2 A DAY IN THE DEVELOPING WORLD

'There is no trust more sacred than the one the world holds with children. There is no duty more important than ensuring that their lives are free from fear and that they can grow up in peace.' These immortal words were spoken by Kofi Annan, former secretary general of the United Nations, speaking about child labour in March 2007.

In June 2010 my editor challenged me to write an article on third world poverty. He wanted the readers to question how any-one could live on less than two dollars a day. The take away Americano he was drinking cost three dollars. So, I set about lo-cating a family in one of the poorest places in the world to spend time with, then to tell their story and show how the impossible is possible.

In January 2011 I arrived in the city of dreams, Mumbai, India to spend three days with a Punjabi family. In Mumbai sixty per cent of people live in the slums. The Punjab family live in Dharuai with their twin daughters and son.

My first experience of Mumbai was deceptive. I arrived in a modern airport, travelled in an air conditioned taxi to a five star hotel. The next morning I made my first visit to the Punjabs. I was greeted by a small man who went by the name of Saba. The strong smell of raw sewage drifted through the air, a small trench ran along the side of the road which raw sewage ran down. After half an hour I had vomited on three occasions and was gasping for air. Saba told me there was no clean drinking water in Dharuai. Twenty-seven per cent of people living in Mumbai do not have access to clean drinking water!

We arrived outside the Punjab home. It was a small humble slum held together by mud and water. Inside sat a family of smiling faces, a family living on less than two dollars a day. Jamal was the eldest and the only one who went to school. In India education is a means of escape. It was the Punjab's hope that Jamal will qualify as an engineer and rescue the family from the slums. Jamal is only fifteen years old.

The next day the twins, Latika and Labori, brought me to the place where they work, for less than a dollar a day. As I approached a set of stairs in a dark building two well built Indian guards stood in my way. Sixty-eight per cent of children living in Dharuai work as labours. Thirty-two per cent work in the stone crushing industry where Latika and Labori work. Children who work on such sites have their natural life expectancy age reduced to thirty-nine years of age. Common illnesses that accompany stone breaking are tuberculosis, silicosis and lung cancer. I thought back to the five star hotel and realised that it was another world away now. Latika and Labori's lives are as hard as the stones they break.

Infant mortality rate in Mumbai is seventy-five per hundred births. Ninety-seven per cent of births in third world countries are home births and occur without any hospital facilities. Many mothers are uneducated and do not know about the importance of hygiene and how to care for a new born baby. Many babies are given baby food in water that is not boiled. This leads to gastroenteritis which leads to diarrhoea, dehydration and, in may cases, death. Families who live on less than two dollars a day are more likely to experience a high infant mortality rate. Children from these families suffer from malnutrition. Every four seconds a child dies from malnutrition, starvation and lack of clean water in the third world. From the time you started to read this essay, about forty children have died from one of these causes. I looked around the streets of Dharuai and wondered, will anyone of these children survive until their next birthday?

On the final day of my visit to Dharaui I went to see the job that Dalaya, the mother of the Punjab family, does. She works in a sweat shop where she makes five dollars a week, less than her two daughters make. Most women only earn seventy-one cents a day working in a sweat shop in Mumbai. The goods they produce are sold for one hundred and twelve times more than what the workers are paid. Women who work in sweatshops can work shifts for up to sixty hours at a time with no break. Dalaya has worked in a sweatshop since she was thirteen years old. She is now thirty-six and has earned just $5,980 since she was thirteen years of age. I thought back to the week before when I bought a new television for the same price it was paid for out of my bonus.

On the final night I shared a meal with the Punjab family. I had decided not to eat the small bowl of rice and I gave it to the twins, who had both developed heavy colds. Amongst all the poverty, the dying and the fear, the Punjabs faced each day with hope. A simple family gathering brings laughter and smiling all around. The family live on less than two dollars a day, yet they have each other and have hope that things will change for them, the hope that Jamal will receive a good education and take his family away from poverty.

I arrived back to my five star hotel less than a mile away from where the Punjabs lived. I noticed two small children standing in the hotel lobby screaming. Behind them stood their mother who was trying to convince her children to eat. I stopped and thought back to the meal in the Punjab home. These two families really were worlds apart.

SHORTLIST – JUNIOR

Catherine Ní Dhubháin

Coláiste Ide, An Daingean, County Kerry, Ireland, Age 13

THE FUTURE OF A CHILD BORN TODAY IN THE DEVELOPING
WORLD

I will admit when I was told I would be stationed in Niger, to write an article about 'the future of a child in Africa', I was a bit nervous. So I decided to do some research. Niger is located in Western Africa. The population is 12.5 million, and it is one of the ten poorest countries in the world. For some reason I knew this would be an unforgettable journey.

After the long, tiring flight, I walk down the street of Niger's capital, Niamey. I notice a group of children, coming from different directions, all heading around the corner. As I follow them, they all head into a freshly built building that stands out from the rest of the slums around the street. Unsurprisingly, this is where I am heading as well.

It is technically an orphanage, but it has been named the 'safe house' by the organizers. As I enter the building, I meet Miranda who I talked to on the phone earlier. She begins giving me a tour, and starts telling me about the organization. 'The aim of the organization is for somewhere the children can go, and play after school. Get fed, have a place for them to go at weekends, and we take in children who have been abandoned or are orphans.'

We go into the nursery and babies are curled up in cots, or being fed by the full time nurses there. 'This little one arrived to us today.' Miranda indicates to a baby in the far corner. I peep into the cot, he looks only 7 months old. I'm shocked to hear he is actually 1 year old. But as I hear, it's not unusual for a child to be underweight, in Africa alone 850 million people are at risk of hunger. Another 700 million don't have enough water. Poverty isn't going empty for a day, and getting something to eat the next. Poverty is going empty with no hope for the future.

It's shocking to think that water and sanitation would only cost $9 billion, but in Europe alone we spend $14 billion on ice cream each year. But Africa is also the same country that pays $20 million every five days, repaying old debts. I repeat, $20 million.

I looked at this beautiful little baby, so fragile and small. How did he get here? I couldn't imagine anybody giving this child up for the world. 'Where are his parents?' I questioned, but I knew the answer before she said it. 'AIDS', Miranda says shortly, shaking her head, 'most of the children here lost their parents to it.'

It is estimated that 33.2 million people are living with HIV, but though most people think that only adults have HIV and AIDS, unfortunately nearly 2 million children under 14 years old are HIV positive. But how could this be happening, when a child dies every 3 seconds from AIDS. The simplest answer is education. The people in Africa don't have enough education to understand what HIV and AIDS are.

It just occurs to me that, without realizing it, I could name more than a dozen things this child could get, and die from, before he's five; things that can be cured by vaccines and medicine all around the world. So far this child's life looks very bleak. I express my thoughts to Miranda and she agrees, but she assures me that this child could be given something that could change all that. Education, it's not a cure, but it's a future.

With an education this child could be anything he wants to be. In most countries it's the law that every child is entitled to a education. But in Africa only 57% of children are enrolled in primary education, and only two-thirds of the population can read. It amazes me to imagine what these children are missing out on – every child dreams of being a teacher, a president, a astronaut. But none of these can be achieved without an education.

'He's lucky to be a boy,' Miranda cuts in the middle of my thoughts. 'What?' I'm confused, why would being a boy be better?! 'Well gender equality is sill low, woman are still not treated equally. For every 100 boys there are only 83 girls enrolled in primary education, also 70% of those living in poverty are women.'

As we walk out of the nursery, my head is filled with facts and figures, buzzing around my head. Twenty-one euro each month could provide basic health kit to a community, as big as Mozambique. Amazing organizations are trying to get these children's lives back on track, give them a home, a education, a future. UNICEF, Concern, Trócaire and many more all dedicate their work to make these children's lives better.

We head out to the playground. Children are running about and playing, some stop and stare in curiosity. I start imaging a little story in my head. Aoife comes home from school, her mom gives her dinner and she sits down with her family. For the rest of the evening, she might watch television or go outside and play with her friends. Tinia comes home from begging, she makes dinner for her four younger siblings. After, and for the rest of the night, she is cleaning and working around the house.

Looking around the playground, I realize that on paper their lives must seem very different to any other child's. But when they are here, in the 'safe house', they are carefree, happy and at peace.

Africa means 'Beauty' and Africa means 'Love'. Africa is 'Nature' and Africa is 'Life', Africa is 'Culture' and Africa is 'Tradition'. Africa is blessed with all of this across the continent.

But the real beauty I see is not the splendid animals, or the breathtaking sunset. It's the smile on the children's faces that will stay with me forever.

SHORTLIST – JUNIOR

Alasdair Donovan

St. Michael's College, Dublin, Ireland, Age 13

THE FUTURE OF A CHILD BORN TODAY IN THE DEVELOPING WORLD

The only problem we had on the road north from the Kuruma Falls where we crossed the River Nile was rain. It started at dusk and hit the windscreen as though it were silver bullets. The driver's response was to go faster. Get to Ghulu more quickly despite the scores of cars and pedestrians bogged down on the road. Once upon a time we would have had to travel in an armed convoy. This flooded, tarmac road was once controlled by the infamous rebel group the LRA (Lord's Resistance Army). The village we needed to get to was home to some of the Acholi people who have been displaced by the recent civil war. We arrived just in time to witness the birth of Tamuk, the most recent addition to the Marland family. That evening I talked to his father, Omar, about his hopes for his son's future.

Perhaps it's just the cynicism of my profession that I couldn't help but dwell on a scenario that is both bleak and dark. His parents' newly built house is a leaky corrugated-iron shack with no electricity, running water or sufficient sanitation. Since the aid agencies left, diseases have spread like wildfire in this area. His family suffers from malnutrition; as children his parents relied on food supplied from the back of a UN truck. The UN has left now. Tamuk and his family have been left to fend for themselves. All of Tamuk's three siblings have inherited HIV from their parents and the chances are that he has as well. Due to the rampant poverty in his homeland his parents can't afford the medicine needed to slow their development into Aids. Even were he to be lucky enough to escape his parent's ailment all he will inherit is land with disputed boundaries and no tools to farm it. His people's traditional form of currency, cattle, has been stolen by a corrupt and desperate Government. He will have to live in a world where his political masters wish to ignore him, his people and his community due to ties with rebel groups. Omar's biggest fear is that the LRA will come back, seize Tamuk and after torturing him incorporate him into their army. This sad outcome seems all too likely. Africa and many of its countries have many problems and challenges. Very few NGOs have any real voice or influence with the governments and those that have must be careful not to be too critical or risk losing the meager power they have.

Omar surprised me with his positive energy as we sat down for a celebratory meal for his son's successful birth. We dined on the traditional food and drink of his country, Ugali, washed down with a homemade beer called Pombe. Omar's wife Katya, still visibly tired from the birth, joins us at the table. Together they give me a more hopeful scenario.

They hope that Tamuk has not contracted HIV and that when aged six he will be able to attend the school Omar is helping to build in their village. They tell me that with academic qualifications Tamuk could find work with a Chinese entrepreneur as there are many new Chinese businesses around Africa, rebuilding the continent after its decades of civil wars. Perhaps with this experience he could one day start his own business. They tell me their hope that organizations such as 'The Ibrahim Index' led by its inspirational leader Mo Ibrahim will make a difference in removing state corruption both in Government and on the street and in turn force businesses to uphold the country's new minimum wage of 58,000 UGX per month, equivalent to just over 17 euro which less than a third of businesses currently comply with.

While this does not seem like much to those of us in the West, the prospect of earning that little money could radically alter, for the better, Tamuk's life. Tamuk's parents give a grudging thanks to their Government for not abandoning them as they do the street people who make up over 50% of the population. They are hopeful that soon the Government will amend the country's appalling health problems (1 doctor per 20,000 sick) and that Tamuk will not suffer as his siblings do. They tell me that they believe that by the time it comes for Tamuk to retire the Government will have implemented some sort of pension scheme for him to live on.

As I look upon Tamuk asleep in his cot, I mull over what his parents have told me. I see him at age ten. At first he seems to be working in his family's disputed fields trying to make ends meet and rediscover the secrets of farming in these lush grassy plains. This image then changes to him in a classroom copying down what his teacher writes on a blackboard, smiling in his smart school uniform. Now I see him behind a desk working in a smart new office, helping to rebuild his country while living in a five-room apartment in one of Uganda's big cities. As the evening progresses to night I see more and more of these future lives, Tamuk meeting an early death from a curable disease, a sixty-five year old Tamuk sitting on a chair beside a river listing to birdsong while enjoying the benefits of a progressive and uncorrupt government. As my driver and I say our farewells to Omar and Katya I notice that the rain has stopped and a new dawn approaches. As we pass back over the Nile I think to myself that maybe some day like the rain the challenges overhanging the lives of Tamuk and the thousands like him will also clear and that the sun of prosperity will in some way shine upon them.

SHORTLIST – JUNIOR

Hazel Nolan

St. Joseph of Cluny Secondary School, Killiney, County Dublin, Ireland, Age 13

LIVING ON LESS THAN $2 A DAY IN THE DEVELOPING WORLD

Two dollars: One euro forty four cents: One pound twenty five pence. In today's developed world, this will buy you a cheap coffee from a newsagent on the motorway, or a return bus ticket, or even just a spot in a car park. Two dollars. In today's world, this is what workers in the third world earn as their daily allowance.

On minimum wage, working minimum hours, a worker in Ireland will earn six euro ninety-two cents per hour. In one hour this worker has earned approximately three times what a worker in the third world earns per day. How is this fair? How can our world ever completely rid itself of world poverty when it can't even pay one worker in the third world a fair wage? These third world workers earn three times less daily than a worker who has done one hour on minimum wage in the developed world, yet they've overcome battles that most of us will never face in our lifetime, our comfortable, fairly paid, lifetime.

I am 13 years of age, living in a comfortable home, in a middle class area of Dublin, going to a fee-paying, well-resourced school. I won't legally be able to work until I am 16. Although when I am 16, my main worries will be: Where will my transition year holiday be? What am I going to wear to the next party I go to? It is not probable, however, that I will be worrying about how to put food on the table for my family, or how I'm going to survive tomorrow.

That would be depriving me of my childhood, and that would be more damaging than I could ever imagine. Even if I went through all the bad things possible for me to experience in my life situation, I probably wouldn't even be on the brink of what the people of the third world go through. I could lose a family member, lose my friends, lose my money, but I could go to a rehabilitation facility, or contact a support group, possibly live in a shelter. Third world people do lose family members, they don't have social networking, so they can't religiously message their friends, and they don't have money. Yet they can't go down to their local community centre and pick up a selectable amount of leaflets on where they can go to improve their life. They must face whatever is given to them, and they must do this without a choice.

Poverty leaves no choice. All the 1.7 billion people living in poverty in our world symbolise that, and this is accentuated by the painful illegal child labour and child trafficking worldwide, for these children are stripped of any sense of being able to choose their life path when they are forced to work instead of getting an education.

In India, a worker at a cotton farm earns about twenty thousand rupees, or two hundred and seventy British pounds . . . in four years. That is a low weekly wage in the developed world. This means they earn twenty pence a day. Twenty pence wouldn't buy you a glass of water in the developed world, yet they earn this daily. Often, workers in the cotton picking industry work long hours and become unhealthy due to pesticide fumes, and it is not uncommon for people to start working at as young an age as twelve years old either. This means if they work until they are sixty five years of age, they will earn approximately three thousand eight hundred and sixty nine pence in their working lifetime. That is what a developed world worker may earn in around two months.

In Ivory Coast in West Africa, child workers in cocoa plantations also work in unjust conditions. They work from six in the morning until six thirty in the evening and are aged twelve to fifteen. At the plantations, they must use machetes to cut off the cocoa pods and then split them open and take out the beans. Usually the farmers who own the cocoa farms send out people to find new workers. These worker scouts travel to neighbouring countries or villages of Ivory Coast and convince young boy's parents that these boys will receive honest work once they reach Ivory Coast and be able to send home their wages to the family. Instead, these boys are forced to work in cocoa plantations, and they are completely disconnected from their family. Often they have no contact with their families and don't return home for years, if ever. They work for nothing.

Hong Kong in China was home to two thousand child workers in 2005. They worked in jobs such as dumping garbage, as sweatshop workers, and collecting recyclable items such as newspapers, aluminium cans, and cardboard. Their work hours ranged from seven hours to twenty-three and a half hours. Sixty per cent of them gave all their earnings to their parents. They earned as little as 156 Hong Kong dollars, or fourteen euro and fifty cent per month, meaning their daily wage was fifty cent in euro.

These three paragraphs have shown you just how little workers in the third world earn worldwide. So when you ask your parents for a new iPod, phone, or camera, think about this article, and hopefully you'll remember just how fortunate you are.

It's quite ironic how these cases of poverty make us realise how materialistic we are, and yet cause us to ask a very materialistic question; does money make the world go round? Does it really buy happiness?

If fair laws were brought in to protect the rights of third world workers, lives would be saved. Where is the justice in these situations? There is none. Sooner or later poverty is going to affect us in a more severe way than we've ever imagined, unless it is stopped. We need democracy. We need justice. We need equality. And we need them in every city, of every country, of this world. However, unlike most of life's necessities, these things come free.

Shortlist – Junior

Hadiah Ritchey
Home School, Eubank, Kentucky, USA, Age 12

Living on Less than $2 a Day in the Developing World

CAMEROON, WEST AFRICA – Scattering underfed chickens through multiple compounds in Cameroon, I make my way very slowly past small faces in dark doorways. The flowers are shriveling in the hot sun, though they reveal signs of better days. The roads are not deserted. People walk by with logs and baskets balanced on their heads with amazing skill. Children run past in the dust, smiling as they are chased by friends. Green can still be seen in the near-by valleys, though the dry season is well under way and water is scarce. Finally, I arrive at my destination, a small compound on the edge of the seemingly hostile village.

I stoop through the low doorway and step into the dimly lit interior. N'gala Jerry and Mosami Constance greet me at the door. Their four children and two nephews slip outside. As we sit on the plastic chairs crowded around a table, Constance tells me of their life. The family is very thankful that Patience, Erasmus and Samwell (their oldest children) are enrolled in the near-by government school even though the walk is nearly an hour. 'They now have hope,' Jerry tells me. 'We do not know if we will be able to send Raisia, Ronald or Felix to school, but we are hoping so hard. Right now the children are working on the farm where we have cassavas and banana trees. If there is any food left over today, we will sell it at the market tomorrow. Yet it is the dry season, so there most likely will be no food to sell.'

Jerry works at the nearby Baptist medical center during the day, which consists of sweeping floors and changing sheets. From 6.00 pm to 12.00 am he is a night guard for the medical store room. Constance was a seamstress but has been unemployed for the past three months and is helping on the family farm, about half the size of a typical suburban yard. Raisia was working as a tutor for some children at the government school, but all together the family makes about $70 a month. Spread out, each person has roughly $0.30 a day to live on. If a tool breaks or a child has medical needs, the only option for help is from extended family members. Food comes from unreliable sources. Often times all they have is what they grow, and that is hardly anything.

Both Jerry and Constance grew up in this village; neither one has ever left it, except for the rare taxi trips to the nearby city of Bamenda. They have no way to escape from the devouring wheel of poverty. No one can get out because Constance and Jerry do not have the education to get a better job. In order to get further education they would need resources of money and hope, both of which are scarce. So the crushing wheel turns on. The whole family is hoping that the children's education will get them out of the economic hole they are in, but even that is unlikely because of the country's unemployment rate. They have no escape. We all stood after the meal of fou-fou and njamma. Jerry escorted me to the door and firmly shook my hand with a smile. Even in the face of extreme poverty, he was smiling like there was no tomorrow, and indeed, there might not be. Walking away I mulled over all I had just heard. I had been complaining over traffic just a week before; now, I just met a man who was not complaining that he usually went without food to feed his family. Quietly, I passed the same flowers I had seen earlier. They appeared all the more amazing knowing what they must have gone through just to be alive.

SHORTLIST – JUNIOR

Aoife Troxel

Dominican College, Taylor's Hill, Galway, Ireland, Age 15

THE FUTURE OF A CHILD BORN TODAY IN THE DEVELOPING WORLD

I feel rivulets of sweat trickling down my back as the jeep jerks over the stony track. Even the mountains look parched. Glancing at the wilted trees lining the road, I think about how I have come to be bouncing around in a 25-year-old jeep through a country that is foreign to me, foreign but not unknown. I was born here thirty years ago but returned to Europe with my parents. To look at me it is striking how little you can see of my birthplace, no trace of the rich dust and leafy trees or the egrets that sometimes soar overhead, in my pale arms and neat clothes.

I am travelling through the old country, an area of rural desolation that seems melancholy for lack of people. Wild nature invades deserted shacks and plants creep to the verge of the road, bursting up through cracks that they laboriously force open.

Two days ago I visited a school. Amid the too-familiar smell of waxy crayons I watched the young teacher effortlessly keeping her pupils in order. From the back of the room, I contrasted it with my own school days. Paper airplanes, thumb tacks, and

28

bubblegum seemed to have no place in this classroom: 'So few of them have the chance to come to school. An education is a blessing,' the teacher told me.

The students wore a pale blue uniform, impeccably clean, and I found my mind drifting to how they achieved it with the dust. When it is dry, every footfall summons up a cloud of thick choking dust that settles in your hair and on your clothes. Trying to brush it off only produces a smear of colour. 'Dedication,' the teacher said softly, smiling at the children. She pointed out a young girl, the top of the class. 'Johanna will be someone important some day,' she said confidently. But I couldn't help thinking, *what if she won't?*

What if circumstances drag her down? If she finishes her education only to find there is no place for her here? No job for her to fill, no chance for her to escape. So she marries young, to a man she thinks she loves. She becomes pregnant quickly. She is ecstatic but it is a hard pregnancy. She miscarries and her husband is angry.

Johanna, frail from her pregnancy, cannot defend herself against his rage. Every day she wakes up multi-coloured with bruises and goes to sleep with more. She becomes pregnant again but she doesn't want it. So she visits a woman, a woman who is supposed to help. Everything goes wrong. Johanna imagines she can feel knives stabbing her from inside. Blades claw at her stomach and thighs, but when she opens her eyes nothing is there, just brown, crusted blood and a great pain in her body and mind.

She returns to her house and her husband. She thinks he will at least let her work for her food. But he is not there, and another family is living in her house. They look on her in pity but do not help.

Johanna staggers out and sleeps by the road. During the night she wakes to an ominous drumming and sees a coffin being borne towards the sea. She shivers and tries to sleep again, but it is useless. She painfully stands and attempts to shuffle forwards.

The morning dawns pale blue and a gentle wind skips through the trees. A doctor arrives at the hospital and approaches the entrance. There is a woman curled in the doorway. She is skeletally thin and her clothes hang on her like folds of paper. He tries to wake her but she will not open her eyes. He touches her arm and finds it cold and stiff. Johanna is dead. I shudder at the thought. She should not die. She is only eight but she is destined for greatness. Her teacher said so.

Circumstances will not drown her. She will leave school, the best student there, and travel to the city. A small city by my standards and a poor one, but there she will find employment. Through thrift and hard work she will slowly save. There will be setbacks. A thief might find her savings, but she will begin again. Her employer might become ill, but she will find another job. In time her savings will be substantial. She moves to a better area of the city. There she meets a man called Patrick. He has set up a school and feeds twenty children every day. He has a job for her. She will be a teacher. In this occupation she finds satisfaction, and she sees in her students the same potential that her teacher saw in her. The school grows and so does the number of children being fed. Sometimes food is so scarce that everyone goes to bed hungry. It kills her inside to see the children suffering.

One day a European couple visits her. A couple like my parents, or like me and my wife. They tell her they want to help. They organise the financing of a new school. Johanna cannot contain her excitement for the children.

Patrick marries Johanna soon after the school is completed. In a few years they will have children. Each tiny baby she will give birth to in a maternity ward. They will name the first one after her teacher and the others after the European couple. One will die. Johanna will be devastated but she knows that tragedies happen every day. Eventually she will live for her husband and other children, but she will never forget.

And I won't forget her. The jeep springs over a stone and I sway in the seat. When I reach the airport I slow. For the first time I have a connection with this place. I feel a pang of sadness and regret. I am leaving the country I have discovered is my home.

But I will be back.

SHORTLIST – JUNIOR

Megan Ferguson

St. Vincent Ferrer High School, New York, USA, Age 14

IMAGINING THE LIFE OF A CHILD BORN TODAY IN THE DEVELOPING WORLD

I sat at my computer the night before my trip to Niger. I was going to volunteer in a small village in a country with the 11th highest mortality rate in the world, and I refused to go to there being ignorant. I type Niger into the search bar and a feeling of dismay comes over me at once: '1/2 of child deaths occur in Africa.' '1/6 of children in Niger die before their 5th birthday.' '66% of the country's population lives below the poverty line.' The facts were devastating.

I thought of all that I had read the previous night and it made my flight unbearably gloomy. I was nervous for the next week and what I was about to experience. I was drove to the home in which I would be living in for the next 7 days. The air was dry for it had not rained in 2 weeks so opening the backseat window didn't nearly satisfy my overheated self.

A young girl, later introduced to me as Djamila, stood on the dry lawn barefoot pounding millets which would later be turned into porridge. I was expecting the family to not only look but act deprived but I was wrong. The mother, Harisa, holding her one year old son Louali, kept her and her six children lively by dancing and singing and it kept their home feeling like a home should feel.

The day went by so smoothly that I had never had a chance to think about food, that is, until I glanced at my watch which read 8.00 o'clock. Harisa let her children stay home from the fields that day being that it was their first time with company, and my first night staying in their home. I refused to allow myself to ask the family about what would be served for dinner not wanting to appear rude but my stomach didn't agree. The loud sound of gurgling coming from the pits of my body startled the children. My cheeks turned red in embarrassment but the interested family refused to let the sound escape conversation. The sound was unfamiliar to them being that their bodies were mostly immune to the hunger. Suddenly the idea of dinner escaped my mind and didn't feel so important anymore.

In need of a moment alone I asked, 'May I use your bathroom please?'

Hearing of the luxury of a bathroom from their schoolhouse, the children knew what I meant and Djamila volunteered to escort me to their 'bathroom'. She led me outside and brought me down a long road and there stood the place that I despised for the next few days ahead of me. Barely touching the old wood I opened the door to the outhouse-like-place. I stepped inside and immediately held my nose and the words from the article I read in class a few months back repeated in my head. 'The lack of safe water and sanitation as well as malnutrition contributes to half of child deaths in the developing world making two-thirds of all deaths preventable.'

Unable to withstand the stench any longer I ran out casually and I caught Djamila staring at me embarrassed, yet sympathetic. I caught myself feeling embarrassed at the thought of taking such a luxury to them for granted. My first day in Niger was not nearly over for it was time for 'nighttime chores' but I was ready for it to be over, ready for a fresh start.

I was awoken by the commotion in the home. Djamila, becoming quite comfortable with me, had made me aware that today her and her siblings not including Louali would be back to attending school. Louali on the other hand would be brought to a nutritionist along with Harisa and I for he is terribly underweight and needs to be measured.

At the nutritionist, Louali was weighed and measured for his height and unfortunately the woman determined that his height to weight ratio is less than 60% of normal making him 10% away from being classified as severely malnourished. Harisa was given high nutrition, therapeutic food to feed Louali so that he may become his appropriate weight. Harisa informed me as well as the nutritionist that they had just arrived home from searching for food for their crops were not growing well this season. I had to admit that I was becoming attached to this lovely family and the thought of them suffering made my heart ache. Something needs to be done.

According to UNICEF approximately 2/3 of child deaths are preventable being that they are caused by things such as diarrhea, malaria, and malnutrition. Most deaths can be prevented by 'cost-efficient measures' such as vaccines and antibiotics. The reduction of child mortality is the fourth of the United Nations Millennium Development Goals. It is up to us to help children like Louali who were born a year ago or children like Djamila who were born up to ten years ago in a developing country. With classes for family care and breastfeeding practices Harisa would be more efficient at keeping her children healthy. There is no need for such a large per cent of children to have to suffer and die before turning five and with all of our technology this misfortune can be prevented.

PASSAGES – JUNIOR

Sarah Benson

Sacred Heart School, Clonakilty, Cork, Ireland, Age 13

THE FUTURE OF A CHILD BORN TODAY IN THE DEVELOPING WORLD

She was born today, a beautiful baby girl. She is intelligent, confident full of energy and potential which could help her to proceed to do well in the world. But she was born into our world in the wrong place at the wrong time so her life might just go to waste. But this isn't the first time that this has happened. She is one of the billion children living in poverty today with no adequate shelter, no clean water and a lack of food. Her mother earns 1 dollar 60 cents a day and does everything she can to raise essential funds for her loving family. But still she is losing this battle against poverty which upsets her deeply.

Her mom started out life just like her. Her name is Taona. She grew up in Malawi, a developing country in south east Africa. She too was an intelligent and confident girl, wanting to help anyone around her who was struggling. She got up each morning at dawn and walked two miles to get water from a well with her mother. She wove baskets and helped to pick grain to help make a living for herself and her siblings. She never got an education though, for a number of reasons. She was poor, it took an hour to get to the school and she was a girl which meant that she had to stay at home and learn about rearing children and doing housework. If you are reading this and thinking – Lucky her! No school!

– think again. She is 29 now and still can't read or sign her name. In fact almost 40 per cent of Malawi's population can't.

Taona played games like jump rope and tag with her friends and loved to lie under the stars at night and watch them twinkle. It pained her mother to see her daughter who was as bright as the stars she gazed at, wasting away with little of her basic needs being met. So she decided to try and make her life the best she could. One day after saving up all her money (which – by the way – wasn't very much) Taona's mother (Mercy) put her children to bed and told them she was going to go to Lilongwe, the capital, and that she wouldn't be returning for possibly a few days. Her children reluctantly agreed to part with their mother and so she left.

… Mercy met other families just like hers on the way, who kindly gave her small amounts of food and water to help her on her way. She never reached Lilongwe because she was so exhausted. She did however find a man selling cloth. She decided to count up her money and buy some cloth to make new clothes for her children. She stopped on the way home to sew the cloth together the best she could. She was good at sewing. She made a beautiful dress for each of her children and made slippers with the leftover material.

Mercy then decided to continue on her way home. Unfortunately on her way home she picked up an illness and wondered if she should return in case her children would pick it up too, but she had to because she had promised her children that she would return to them. She arrived home to find her children starving and sick.

There wasn't enough money to buy medicine so the children's health soon got worse. One of her children passed away but luckily the others got better. Mercy's health, however, was still quickly deteriorating.

… Stories like this happen all the time, in fact from the years 2000–2009, 88 million children died. Instead of spending 11 billion

US dollars on ice cream in Europe in 1998, we could have given every child in developing countries an education. So next time you're trying to pick what flavour ice cream you would like, think about the children who really need that money.

She was born today, a beautiful baby girl. She is intelligent, confident full of energy and potential which could help her to proceed to do well in the world. But she was born into our world in the wrong place at the wrong time so her life might just go to waste.

But we can help her.

Olwyn Bell

Tallaght Community School, Dublin, Ireland, Age 15

THE FUTURE OF A CHILD BORN TODAY IN THE DEVELOPING WORLD

… So while we are complaining about our life being unfair try being in the shoes of a child in Africa. A child that doesn't have as much as we have. A child that might never know what it's like to have fun, travel the world or living a life that we take for granted. It would be hard for us to imagine what people have to go though in Africa and other third world countries. Imagine what it would it like to watch children at the age of five dying well before their time because of malnutrition and poverty. There are people who don't even have homes and children are dying everyday of diseases that nobody can cure. If you just help people who are in need, it would make you are better person. Imagine the feeling of knowing you saved someone's life and help make someone's life easier. You wouldn't like it if you were going though this. Having to go though not having any where to live, clothes to wear or having no one to look after you. Everyone deserves to laugh, smile and have a childhood but nobody deserves to go though this no matter what they have done. So the next time you think your life is unfair or your life sucks, think about what people have to go though ever yday of their lives.

Lucy Collins

Loreto Secondary School, Fermoy, County Cork, Ireland, Age 13

LIVING ON LESS THAN $2 A DAY IN THE DEVELOPING WORLD

Imagine living on two dollars a day! You would have none of the luxuries that people take for granted. You would have no running or clean water, no land to call your own, no properly built insulated house, no hospital, no medicine and often no chance of an education. You could barely survive. People do survive but they have to go through life and try. Communities must work together to earn enough money to pay for everything each person needs. They themselves wonder how they make ends meet. These people's rights are not being met and we need to do something about it!

During my time in Africa I travelled through a small town in Sudan called Jabrin. The houses were hovels made of mud and sticks. I was shocked at the conditions of the people's homes and lives. I met a small boy called Taahir meaning pure and modest. He was seven years old and lived with his father and sisters. His mother had died giving birth, as many women in developing countries do because she had not got the medical attention she needed.

I was staying nearby in the only well-built house in the village. I remained in the town for a few days and I watched him. He was wary as he had seen too many strangers do terrible things to children. He had had to grow up fast and had missed his childhood. Every day he got up at dawn and went to work with no breakfast. He worked on the small piece of land his father had rented from a rich farmer and that the whole family worked on. They grew bananas and fig trees. He hated picking bananas as his fingers be-

38

came bruised and sore. This was how his family made a living. He picked and tended the bananas for one hour then ran home and ate a small bowl of sorghum, a porridge-like dish. He ate two small meals a day. He was thin and wiry.

… Taahir dreams that he will have opportunities that his parents didn't have and that his family will not have to live on so little money. Please help Taahir's dreams come true by giving and helping. Many children's dreams and hopes for a better future don't happen due to suffering and disease. Please remember, every five minutes a child dies in Africa. Don't let it be him.

Laura Beth Collister

Ramsey Grammar School, Isle of Man, Age 15

LIVING ON LESS THE $2 PER DAY IN THE DEVELOPING WORLD

When I agreed to travel to India, I thought I knew exactly what I would get out of it. I had it all figured out before I'd even arrived in the place. I planned to write about the poverty-stricken families, severe starvation and the sheer destitution of the people who live there, and why richer countries like the UK should be helping them. Although all of this would make a valid article, it's not the same as hearing the story from the perspective of a person who actually has to contend with it all on an everyday basis. Of course I'd be lying if I said I wasn't greatly affected by the overwhelming hardship these people are forced to deal with, as it's clearly a major issue. However, I discovered much more than I originally expected to find in rural India. In fact, I couldn't have been more surprised.

I arrived at the house of the Korpals, an extremely deprived family living in what I can only describe as unrelenting squalor.

They welcomed me with great attentiveness and warmth, which I honestly didn't expect at all, for whatever reason I do not know. Their house was extremely confined, as well as dirty, damp and extremely dark. They showed me a tiny living room, an even smaller kitchen, and two bedrooms for themselves and their two children. The little furniture they had was crumbling to pieces, and it wasn't at all suitable for a family of four. The toilet was around the back of the house in a separate hut, the smell of which was more than I could bear for little more than a second. They told me that it wasn't ideal, but it couldn't be helped as their house was right beside a river to which all the villages' waste ran through.

Ishani, the mother, was obviously worn out. Just by looking at her you could tell she hadn't slept properly in months. She had dark circles under hers eyes that couldn't go unnoticed. Despite this, she smiled so intently whenever I asked about her husband or her children. It was late at night when I had arrived, but she still made sure I was as comfortable as possible in my room before she left me for the evening. When I had gone to bed that first night, I just couldn't get to sleep. It wasn't the smell of damp that lingered on the rotting walls, or the crashing of the rushing river outside, but it was Ishani. She never once complained about the lack of space, food and general living conditions she and her family had to contend with, she just smiled, and carried on. It puzzled me how she could seem so genuinely happy, and yet live in a place like this.

Over the next couple of days I began to understand Ishani's approach to life. Every day she would do at least one thing that really made me think about my own beliefs as well as hers. Early each morning she would wave goodbye to her husband as he left for his day's work at the market stalls, and said she was thankful that they were lucky enough for him to have a job at last. The Korpals had almost nothing at all, but I could see that they all considered themselves extremely fortunate to have each other. I wondered whether the Korpals had ever really thought about leading a different life. Had they ever thought about having the chance to see the rest of the world, or to have a better home, or even just to be able to send their children to a school? I couldn't imagine a life where these opportunities were never even considered, just ruled out completely because they had accepted that they are, and always will be, in the poverty trap.

... When I had to leave the Korpals, I knew for certain that I had changed, but the Korpals hadn't. They seemed to accept that when I left, that would be the last they would ever see or hear from me ever again. Not only had I gained a tremendous amount of respect for Ishani and her family, but everyone else around the world that was going through a similar situation to her... They taught me that if you have nothing else in life, you have no real home, very little food, and an extremely low income; your family is often the one and only thing that will stand by you.

Marco Tessaro

The English International School of Padua, Italy, Age 14

LESSONS WE CAN LEARN FROM THE DEVELOPING WORLD

I think that people that suffer every day to live with less than $2 a day should be awarded a golden medal because they survive in the most horrible conditions and still try to see the good part of what they are doing and sharing every bad and good moment with the family. I personally can't see me doing this. Every day I buy something worth more than $2. In one day I might also spend $200 for a computer or $70 for a PS3 game while children in these poor countries are satisfied with so little. I think that we all should learn from these people because they will teach us how to live a real life and not what we think as fashion and technology but the least needed.

Sabhin O'Sullivan

Loreto Secondary School, Balbriggan, Dublin, Ireland, Age 13

LIVING ON LESS THAN $2 A DAY IN THE DEVELOPING WORLD

... Almost 80% of humanity live on less than $10 a day, and over 22,000 children die each day due to poverty. Over 72 million children are not in school due to poverty, and 57% of them are girls. Every year there are 300–350 million cases of malaria worldwide, and 1.1 billion people have no access to clean water, with a further 2.6 billion lacking basic sanitation. Now, these facts may just seem like digits on paper, but they are much more than that. They are people's lives, people as innocent as we are, people who die unfairly. Almost all of us get to live our lives happily without coming across such disasters, but far too many people are not promised that simple lifestyle.

Twelve-year old Samba lives with his family of eleven in a house made of dried mud. Neither of his parents can find work, and so he and his three younger brothers (as girls are rarely able to find work) work at a carpet factory for twelve hours a day. They only get a twenty-five minute break, and if the work is not done right, they are either beaten or their break-time is taken from them. Children are cheaper to hire than adults, and their small wage has to provide for the whole family.

... Could you put yourself in Samba's shoes and live his life-style? Think of that next time you throw out your food, or complain that 'everyone' else you know has the Wii and you don't. Millions of people would not be starving if we shared our food around. Over two-thirds of good, edible food is thrown out from rich areas like Australia, North America and Europe a year, and so much of that is provided by people in the third world. Bananas, cocoa beans and coffee beans are three examples of produce we receive from unfairly-paid farmers. How many kids toss their half-eaten bananas in the bin when mummy isn't looking? How many of us take chocolate for granted – doesn't matter if it falls on the ground and gets dirty, there's never a shortage here. How many parents have half the pot of tea or coffee and pour the rest down the sink?

Another way of seeing how different our lives are to those in developing countries is our appreciation for animals. We drive past fields of cows, goats and donkeys every day, and we don't even think about what they're worth. Donkey – oh, it's a dumb old animal, worth nothing, no help to the world at all. What's the point of him? If we were given a donkey, we'd probably say to the giver – are you nuts? But to a child in Nigeria, he'd be the best present they'd ever received.

...Going back to the $2 nightmare, how can that much supply our whole family's daily food, education, medication and clothing needs? How do so many families do it? That's an answer we all want to know. Another common question is what can we, as citizens of a rich country, do about it? There are answers to that question...

43

Lucy Smith-Williams

Gainesville, Tennessee, USA, Age 15

LIVING ON LESS THAN $2 A DAY IN THE DEVELOPING WORLD

I have been stationed for the last month in India, a prominent developing world country. Being able to see first-hand how these people live on less than $2 a day has really shown me not only how hard it is, but how remarkable it is. Two-thirds of Indians live on less than $2 a day. Many studies have been done, which reveal that the $2 a day figure doesn't mean $2 a day. It means instead, very small payments and sometimes very long periods of time with very little to no income at all. The world's poor spend huge amounts of their time, energy, and ingenuity managing and sorting out the finances that they do have. They save, borrow and repay in cash but mostly in kind. It is remarkable that they do so without formal mathematical education. At best they might have acquired a miniscule amount of literacy.

A family that lives on $2 a day has specific worries that overwhelm them every day. Their first concern would be getting food on the table. They have a constant worry in the back of their minds of what will end up on their table at the end of the day.

... I have interviewed a local illiterate couple involved in a whole range of complicated financial structures and deals. As you may be asking yourself, how can they be involved with a complicated arrangement of their financial needs without being able to read or write? They replied with bagged eyes and solemn faces that they 'talk about it all the time and that fixes it into their memories. These things are important, they keep you awake at night.' ...They told me that working and dealing with other people about their money was not exactly preferable but if you're poor, it is a necessity with no other alternative. They looked at me with grave eyes when they remarked, 'We only do it to survive.' These people, micro-savers of the Indian slums, are like the two and a half billion others like them in India, living on less than $2 a day.

Observing the daily struggle of these families has been a sobering experience, and at times has felt almost unbearable. I am astonished at the persistence, the creativity and the resourcefulness of these people. When I first tried to imagine living on $2 a day I thought it would be a simple, though painful daily chore. As I got to know and understand these families I realized that living on such a meager sum requires a tremendous amount of thought and care and skill, and I have great respect for the people I have begun to know here in India.

Sophie Rhatligan Walsh

St. Joseph of Cluny Secondary School, Killiney, Dublin, Ireland, Age 14

THE FUTURE OF A CHILD BORN TODAY IN THE DEVELOPING WORLD

A few years ago my sister gave birth to a beautiful baby girl, Rebecca. She weighed seven pounds nine ounces and was perfect; the couples' first bundle of joy. They were so excited on the arrival of their first child and bought every baby book ever written, just to be on the safe side.

From the first moment that baby was born, she was promised a very bright future. She would never grow hungry, cold, would never have to worry about an education as her parents will provide that for her. There will always be a roof over her head because her parents will always work hard to provide her with the best.

My sister was discharged the next day as there was nothing wrong with the tiny child. She was completely perfect in every way, she had no disabilities, no health issues and there was nothing to worry about.

Now imagine living in the sweltering heat of a country such as Malawi in the same year, where there is no health centre within walking distance. There is a mother, Asyi, who has just given birth to a baby boy, Dayo. Although his name translates as 'joy arrived', there is no happiness or joy as he is born malnourished – less than three pounds and two ounces. His bones protrude outwards. He is merely a skeleton. Unfortunately, Asyi suffers from HIV and AIDS and if she was to feed her baby breast milk, he would then suffer from this terrible disease as well. Like any mother, Asyi wants her son to survive, so she will do anything to keep her child alive. Although in the long run, Dayo will suffer from HIV and AIDS, for now he is surviving on his mother's milk. It's a catch 22. By the age of five or even younger, Dayo will be expected to help and work with his older brothers and sisters to tend and grow the crops. He does not go to school as he is needed at home to help. His childhood is taken away from him completely and he is carrying an enormous burden no five year old should have to bear.

In Ireland at the same time, five year old Rebecca has just started Junior Infants and will start to learn the tedious ABCs and her 123s during this year. As she is only five, her head is still filled with childhood ignorance and bliss. She does not realise how lucky she is to even go to school and learn to read and write. When she and her classmates are asked, 'What do you want to be when you grow up?' and they all answer with outrageous dreams, 'A princess, a pirate, a teacher, an astronaut and a builder.' They all do not realise that all of these dreams can potentially come true if they work and try hard to get what they want. In somewhere like Malawi, all these dreams remain as dreams as they do not have an education to make this dream a reality.

Now travel six years and we see Rebecca and Dayo as eleven year olds both living completely different lives. Rebecca has become wiser and less ignorant of situations but still does not realise how lucky she and her friends are. They do not have to work to provide just a small amount of food for their families. They just have to travel a few metres from their seat watching TV to get a glass of water from their tap or from a filtered fridge. Compare this to Dayo and others like him who have to walk almost three miles to fill buckets of water and travel back those three miles with these extremely heavy buckets, afraid of spilling a single drop as it has to last all day for cooking, washing, drinking and sometime for bathing, if there is any left that is...

Melissa Owusu

St. Vincent Ferrer High School, New York, USA, Age 15

LIVING ON LESS THAN $2 A DAY IN THE DEVELOPING WORLD

Before my time in Zimbabwe I thought the poverty wasn't so bad. I thought organizations like Concern had the situation under control. Unfortunately I was terribly wrong. My job was to only observe and write, but I started to form a bond with the family I was observing. A little girl in particular named Mudiwa captured my heart. For two months I followed her very fragile looking body through the Zimbabwean terrain. Mudiwa is 15 and has a mother, father, and two younger brothers. Pretty average family isn't it? Her father sells a few goods out on the marketplace and her mother is too sick and weak to get an actual job. So she supports the family by being the best housewife she can be to their little shack. Mudiwa's family day doesn't begin because it never ends. The family is always chasing after something to survive – water, milk, a freelance job, anything to help them survive one extra day.

Sanjana Tripathi

Singapore American School, Age 12

LIVING ON LESS THAN $2 A DAY IN THE DEVELOPING WORLD

… So why don't these people just stop being poor? Why can't they just work hard and become rich? This seems the obvious question. The answer lies in the vicious poverty cycle. The poverty cycle includes all the stages of poverty and it goes in this order: Born into poverty, suffering from health problems, lacking education, lacking jobs. Then children are born into this same trap. This cycle is nearly impossible to break for any one person and usually requires outside intervention.

… Poor people do not need to be handed money. Simply handing over money and leaving them just would not work because these people need something more. They need food, water, medicine, homes, education, and a way to support their families. Money alone can't solve all these problems. NGOs, however, can create an umbrella under which all the needs can be met.

So what would it be like to be poor? Whether you are poor due to war, poor due to lack of jobs, or for any other reason, it would be very difficult. You would work more than 16 hours a day. You would never have enough money for basic needs like food or clean water. You would always be unclean and so would

48

get sick often but you will not have enough money for proper medicine. You would not have enough money to go to school. When you get older, you would not be able to get a job because you lack an education and skills. Your children would be born into poverty.

This cycle can be broken. The problem can be solved. People who live on two dollars a day are in a bad situation but we can make it better. There is hope.

Hannah Mason

North Walsham High School, Norfolk, England, Age 14

THE FUTURE OF A CHILD BORN TODAY IN THE DEVELOPING WORLD

… The food the (Rwandan) children eat is based around bananas and plantains, pulse, potatoes and beans. The diet the children eat is high in vegetables but it lacks in animal proteins. I saw children sitting on the sides of the roads begging for money as thin as sticks. They make their own porridge like consistency made out of maize and water called ugali. I was shocked when I realised and thought about us – we go to the shop and buy porridge and eat it, we take these privileges for granted.

… In the UK we do things to help the third world countries such as red nose day (comic relief) sports relief, and live aid. Everyone helps but no one really realises what the people of Rwanda and other countries have to go through and how happy they are when we help them. We all watch the news and ignore the true facts of life, but when you see it before your eyes you cannot walk away from it, you feel guilt within you.

Many people do not realise it because we do not think. We turn a tap on and get fresh clean water, we go to the shop buy a loaf of bread. Just remember that other people do not have these privileges, next time just think when you do these things.

Emma Wheatley

North Walsham High School, Norfolk, England, Age 13

THE FUTURE OF A CHILD BORN TODAY IN THE DEVELOPING WORLD

Rudyard Kipling said, 'east is east and west is west'. This is suggesting that he is saying we are all different so it doesn't matter. But I believe that we are different but everyone deserves a decent standard of living. No child can lead a perfect life, but they can make the most of the one they do have. The children in the UK and such places tend to take things for granted. Think – every time you have a drink (containing water) there is another person somewhere drinking death; with your help we can make a difference to this. Think – every three seconds a child in a third world country dies. Think – every time you go to school there is another child walking miles, for something that they treasure. Think.

… One thing I did learn in my stay was that they never stopped smiling, they had nothing but they did not stop smiling. As I walked with Aabha she was smiling, we were walking fifteen miles. I was crumbling at the knees, she was helping me, it should have been the other way around. After five days with no food I was distraught and empty. I could not bear any more. I decided to build them a well. I went back to the hotel, got food and water. I've never seen a child so grateful in my life me and ten others

50

built a well, this took two days, all the people helped. These people were over the moon, they asked how they could repay us. I simply said, 'don't, you have repaid me enough by helping me realize that no matter what, keep smiling and you will get through'.

Ellen Kinsella

Coláiste Íde, Dingle, County Kerry, Ireland, Age 15

THE FUTURE OF A CHILD BORN TODAY IN THE DEVELOPING WORLD

Martin Luther King once said, 'I have a dream'. Millions of children today dream a dream that harmony will be reunited, that hope will be instilled in their lives, that in a modern world with so much food wasted no one will feel hunger and education will be for all. I don't want to think about a future for a child born in the developing world if it can't be changed. President Obama says 'Yes we can'. I believe in this view. In 1990, 99 million people died in developing countries and in 2009, this was reduced to 60 million. The Millennium Development Goals aim to eradicate poverty and provide health for all women and children by 2015.

... Can the future of a child born in the developing world become one of prosperity, hope and love? Can we eradicate poverty and ensure education for all children? Can all these children live a long, happy life with their family? Can these children explore their talents and let their dreams come alive? I see a future where all children sleep soundly at night, with a full stomach, where there is hope and prosperity and where the Millennium Development Goals have improved the lives of millions of children

51

worldwide. We have to change. Don't we owe it to the 45 children who have died by the time you have finished reading this?

Micaela Depinna

Presentation College, Athenry, County Galway, Ireland, Age 15

LIVING ON LESS THAN $2 A DAY IN THE DEVELOPING WORLD

… Everything I have written up to this point has been selfish. How many times was the word 'me' or 'I' used? The fact is, that locket was something I wanted first and foremost. Not something I needed, like food, water or shelter. A person in Africa has less than $2 per day to live on. Here in Ireland, that would just about get you a loaf of bread, never mind any trinkets like lockets.

The sad thing is, a lot of the time we lose sight of how lucky we are, and we forget about those who haven't as much as us. We forget about necessities and focus on our wants. I want this, I want that. But the reality is, in the developing world, the people living there don't have a chance to think about wants, they have to focus on what they need in order to survive.

So think about that the next time you go to buy something you want but don't need. Think, 'Could this money be used in a more useful, and helpful way?' And if you realise it could be, but can't figure out what to spend it on instead, Concern would be absolutely delighted to receive a donation. Because that donation would allow them to help more people in the developing world to buy all the things they need.

To need is to survive. To want is to dream. Help people survive so that one day, they too can dream.

Libby O'Connor

Millstreet Community School, County Cork, Ireland, Age 14

THE FUTURE OF A CHILD BORN TODAY IN THE DEVELOPING WORLD

... This is just one possible future; there are millions of children living millions of different lives in the developing world. Some of them will have better lives in more developed places, some of them will have poorer lives and harder futures. Some of them have no future as many will die young. The developed world has to realise the shocking reality of what children in the developing world face – poverty, war, famine and disease, because only the developed world has the resources needed so desperately to improve the lives of these children.

Luca Costan

English International School of Padua, Italy, Age 15

LIVING ON LESS THAN $2 A DAY IN THE DEVELOPING WORLD

... The children here like to play football around the narrow paths in this favela. We ask Pablo Jnr. how much he earns a month. He does some calculations and he tells us that he gets 70 dollars. 'It is enough to have food but not enough to have a future,' he says. 'Every day I bring home some fish and some bread, everyone here does some extra, small jobs to earn a few dollars more. For example Roberto sells some of his fish to people while Julio makes carts and sells them to the people who have necessity.' We say goodbye to Junior and walk towards Julio's cart workshop, which is just down the street. While walking we notice that there is a lot of people fishing on small rafts made from scrap materials. There are a lot of children too who are diving in the brown water without concern for the danger they are facing. We walk on and enter Julio's workshop. He's working on a big wooden cart. He stops working and comes towards us, he does not speak English. We ask him for whom he's making the cart. 'I'm building it for a fisherman.' Julio is a big strong man, he doesn't speak a lot but he tells us that he loves his job and it brings him a lot of money. We notice that he wears no protection while working. He tells us that protection is the last of his problems because he now wants to invest all of his money into expanding his business by hiring two assistants in order to make more carts...

Dianna Baez

St. Jean Baptiste High School, New York, USA, Age 15

LIVING ON LESS THAN $2 A DAY IN THE DEVELOPING WORLD

... The next day, we woke up and visited the school. The school was so small and it was very limited. There were no desks, barely any writing utensils, and too many children in only one room. Compared to this school, my school was a luxury! Our flight was due for tonight. We were leaving back to America. The faces of the people were sad, turned off, and they looked so depressed. I noticed every wrinkle and every cut, bruise, scar on the faces of the men and women. Each of those marks had a story concealed deep inside and something tells me that they were all caused by the struggles and hardships these people go through on a daily basis. Even finding a meal to feed their families was a task that needed much strength and endurance. It was certainly no trip to a supermarket.

When we finally got home I threw myself on the sofa and hugged it tightly. My mom asked, 'What was that all about?' I responded, 'Well, I never knew how much work it must be to get a piece of furniture that is so perfect.' My mom gave me the you're-crazy-face. We never really notice the things we have, even the minuscule items. We're lucky to have the house we live in, the slippers we use, the breakfast on our tables every morning, the bed we sleep in, and even the soap we shower with. Visiting the developing world has taught me to be appreciative of what you have even if it is just a toothbrush, because the truth is there are some people who don't even have that.

Jenny Evans

St. Joseph of Cluny Secondary School, Dublin, Ireland, Age 14

THE FUTURE OF A CHILD BORN TODAY IN THE DEVELOPING WORLD

… She continues rocking her child very gently, thoughtful, lost in time, so much so that she doesn't notice her baby softly crying. She asks herself why she was so unfortunate to be born in such a poverty stricken place where even the ground begs for nourishment. Why couldn't she be born with white skin, with a rich family surrounded by a grand house and food in every supermarket around the corner. If only she lived in a country with friendly people with cool, fertile earth to plant crops. If she got enough money she would take her child and leave this dry, dusty hell behind without a backward glance. But she wondered if she could ever make that money. And if she did would they welcome her and her child, an asylum seeker? Would they help her or would they tell her to go home? Would they bully her child at school? She pondered these thoughts, longingly searching for a way to escape to a place that would accept her.

On the opposite side of the street, a baby has died. The mother wailing angrily, shouting at death itself. She pleads with death to bring her baby back, death's black cloak enveloping the child. The mother, moaning and crying, holds her baby so tight it is as if she had finished playing a tug of war game with death, a game in which she could have never won. There is no sound except for the mother's mourning. Death had made everything peaceful, everything feels surreal. It is as if I can feel the world turning, the people breathing, every heart beating...

Ciara Lyons

Loreto Secondary School, Clonmel, County Tipperary, Ireland, Age 14

LIVING ON LESS THAN $2 A DAY IN THE DEVELOPING WORLD

'A New Dawn a New Life'. As you struggle to take your first breath the midwife cuts the cord with a rusty blade. Your mother lays on the damp mud floor of a rural village in Tanzania. She reaches for water in the sweltering heat but only 62% of the population have access to clean drinking water – she unfortunately belongs to the other 38%. The likelihood that she will survive to nurture you is already slim. Your father has died of AIDS which infects 7% of the adult population. Your mother may well be infected but as there is no health worker available to carry out a clinical assessment on you or your mother, your fate is already sealed. Life expectancy here is 44 years of age and as a baby girl these four decades, should you survive, will be the most difficult of your life as you are part of the 73% of the world population who are expected to live on less than $2 a day. It is indeed very likely that you will never see your fifth birthday and that you will be swept into the staggering 10.6 million children in the developing world who die before they reach the age of 5. Let me put this into context – this figure is the same as the child population in France, and Germany, Greece and Spain.

... This article may make this child visible, she has taken her first breath, can we change her destiny? In the words of Barrack Obama, oh 'yes we can' give her birth-rights, dreams, hopes and a fair share of the earth's resources. Don't take her breath away. Give the people of poverty all over the world the chance to live to the full and not have shortages of resources standing in their way. Understanding what the developing world is like is one thing, but living in poverty every day is another thing, waking up every day struggling to survive. It does not bear thinking about what the people of Tanzania go through trying to live on less than $2 a day in the developing world.

Megan Clifford

Holy Family Secondary School, Newbridge, County Kildare, Ireland, Age 14

THE FUTURE OF A CHILD BORN TODAY IN THE DEVELOPING WORLD

… But it doesn't have to be like this, it shouldn't be like this. The country you're born in should have no influence whatsoever on your economic status in the future. Another boy, born at the same time in a wealthy country in a hospital, as opposed to a mud hut, shouldn't be guaranteed an education and a good job in later life, while the boy born in a mud hut is relegated to a life of hard toil on an empty stomach.

The boy born on January 28th at 5.31 am on a shivery night should receive an education. If the people who are exploited on a daily basis can't calculate the cost of producing the coffee beans, they can't see just how much the big MNC players are really abusing them.

He should go to school, he should learn how to read and write, he should have parents who have enough money to feed him, and he should have the choice of what he wants to do with his fifty-five year slice of the apple pie of life.

Each and every person deserves the chance to make something of themselves. One right we have as human beings is the right to the pursuit of happiness. Our country of origin should not affect our opportunities but, unfortunately, it does.

The mother in the mud hut wants the same things the mother in the hospital wants for her son – happiness and a better life than the one they suffered through/enjoyed.

But which mother will have her wishes fulfilled? You do the guesswork for me. I already know how it plays out. The evidence is visible in boardrooms and plantations worldwide.

Emma Lacey

Loreto Secondary School, Clonmel, County Tipperary, Ireland, Age 15

THE FUTURE OF A CHILD BORN TODAY IN THE DEVELOPING WORLD

… However there is a glimmer of hope in Hadi's future and the future of all children in Sudan. The cycle of violence and civil warfare in Sudan, which was generated by the divisions between North Sudan, which is mainly Arab Muslim, and Darfur, which is mainly African Muslim, and South Sudan which is mainly African Christian, may be coming to an end. Sudan's wartime deaths from civil war between 1983 and 2005 amount to more than two million people and the peace agreement signed at the end of that civil war guaranteed a referendum on secession. In January in a historic vote more than 98 per cent of the ballots cast were in favour of independence for southern Sudan.

The result was accepted by Sudan President Omar Al Bashir which paves the way for Southern Sudan to become the world's newest country in July. After decades of death and turmoil, at least now there is hope that life can be different for children born in a new Sudan.

Orla Buckley

Meán Scoil Nua, Castlegregory, County Kerry, Ireland, Age 14

LIVING ON LESS THAN $2 A DAY IN THE DEVELOPING WORLD

... For me this trip served to be a real eye-opening experience. I had become detached from the reality faced by these people; it was only when I experienced it personally that my empathy developed. Conditions need to be improved. The conditions these human beings dwell in are substandard and grossly impoverished. They deserve dignity and respect and should at least be provided with their basic human rights. I appeal to world leaders to make informed decisions about finance and to cease the wastage and with this money saved, transfer it to the overseas aid programme.

The key to improving the situation is to educate the people. The literacy rate in the country is 72%, which is acceptable but efforts could be made to improve it. These people need to be taught the skills of farming and crop production. If we could educate them on how to take care of themselves it would be a major step on the road to recovery. School attendance is very low and rested at 57% in 2000. This figure urgently needs to improve.

Medicine is a factor that needs to be addressed. Vaccines need to be made available and the establishment of clinics is crucial to the strengthening of the population and the overall development of the health of the residents of Tanzania.

Overall my trip to Tanzania served me with a mission and a longing for justice. I hope after reading this article it will inspire you to take action and do your part, however small in changing the life conditions of 'Mia' and her people. Living on $2 dollars a day is their situation at present – take steps to prevent it being the future. Could you allow this to happen?

Muhammad Rehan

Aitchison College, Lahore, Pakistan, Age 15

LIVING ON LESS THAN $2 A DAY IN THE DEVELOPING WORLD

… By now, some people might even be thinking that it is impossible not to starve to death but the developing world has now come with a better philosophy to the situation: 'a friend in need is a friend indeed.' This is an enigma but social and cultural values of humanity have caused the poverty-stricken people to unite and strengthen their social fabric system to face their dilemma. In times of dire need of food, people come together as one whether it concerns devouring food like ravenous wolves or earning money for the little food available. As a matter of fact, I have been lucky enough to conduct my research on the developing world stationed in the sub-continent for the past few weeks and learned how the deprived society living under $2 day are surviving.

The first thing I noticed in this superior bond is that all the poor people usually live together varying from city to city in slums. This helps the cluster to develop a realization for each other as they understand that they are not alone in their depression which in turn unites them as one big extended family. Hence, once they become 'relatives in nature and blood' they are usually willing to make sacrifices for others such as giving up food and nutrition so their 'family' is fed rather than themselves.

... Ultimately, it is important that we learn a few lessons from the developing world. It is incredible to see how even when robbed of all necessities of leading a normal life, the people in the developing world manage to coexist and even share their portion with each other. But social unity and sharing is not their only reason of success as every person in their society is allotted a duty and they follow it sincerely no matter how physically or mentally torturing it is. If we follow just some of these traits it might help to make the world a better place. However the success of the deprived to survive should not be taken as granted since even the strongest social unity will only last so long.

Taofeeqat Olanlokun

Ardgillan Community College, Balbriggan, Dublin, Ireland, Age 13

LIVING ON LESS THAN $2 A DAY IN THE DEVELOPING WORLD

When you think of life for people in developing countries what comes to your mind? Lack of education? World hunger? Diseases and death? All of these mostly affect ordinary everyday children. Most of you or your children have or had good access to education, but do the children of a developing country? No, they do not. Seventy-two million kids around the world never get the chance to go to primary school. Fourteen per cent of all the children in the world are forced to work instead of going to school.

Even though developing countries have eighty per cent of the world's population, they only have fifteen per cent of the world's education spending. These kids depend on their parents to be their educators, but what will their parents have to teach them if they never went to school? This will pass on and on with no end. If these kids do not go to school, how can they manage to get into college or even get a good job in another country? They will end up working day and night in sweat shops, just to earn two dollars a day. How will they be able to support their family? They could end up on the streets and have to beg for a living, they could start stealing which could lead to bigger crimes.

All this just because they had nothing to do with their lives, one of these kids could be the one to end world hunger and change everyone's lives, we never know. All they need is a start, and their start could be from getting good education…

Niamh Doyle

St. Joseph of Cluny Secondary School, Killiney, Dublin, Ireland, Age 14

LIVING ON LESS THAN $2 A DAY IN THE DEVELOPING WORLD

… The reason Dalila has to care for her brother and sister is because her mother has been taken away to hospital. But that was six months ago and Dalila hasn't seen or heard of her mother since. In fact, she does not even know if her mother is still alive. Thousands of children in the slums of Nairobi, like Dalila, end up becoming carers for their families. Dalila and all these other children have the same fears and worries. Each night, Dalila thinks, Will she ever see her mother again? How will she keep her brother and sister safe? How will she continue to get food for them all? Will she even make it through to tomorrow? Dalila's life is a constant struggle for survival and, like most people, Dalila is afraid of the outcome of the future.

I was shocked to learn that so much could be dependent upon a six-year-old girl. Dalila will never be able to go to school while she has to take care of her siblings. I couldn't believe my eyes when I saw the tin hut that Dalila, Sokoro and Kanika called home. Words just failed me. And I'm sure like many, I did not want to believe that such hardship could go on between so many innocent people. Dalila's story was just one of thousands similar.

However, the truth of the matter is, these hardships do go on, all over the world for millions of people. Every day someone in the developing world dies because of starvation. Statistics show that 98% of the world's hungry live in the developing world, 10.9 million children under the age of five die in the developing world, and

60% of these deaths are caused by malnutrition and hunger-related diseases. These statistics are both shocking and upsetting.

Michaela Holland

Scoil Mhuire gan Smál, Blarney, County Cork, Ireland, Age 13

THE FUTURE OF A CHILD BORN TODAY IN THE DEVELOPING WORLD

... The sun can be seen as a rare pleasure in Ireland but can also be seen as a frequent discontentment in Malawi as it can cause plenty of problems such as drought. A drought may sound like complete and utter bliss to our ears but it can cause infections and diseases a lot worse, cause skin cancer, cause a shortage of water which is one of the major maladies in Malawi and cause thousands of deaths each year as a result of little or dirty water that is drunk by the people of Malawi and also make crops and vegetables fail to grow. For the farmers of Malawi their only income sometimes may be a few animals and a patch of land to grow crops. If there is a drought crops can't grow and those people will have no money or food. On the other hand if there is a flood crops will fail to grow as they will receive too much water. These natural disasters are problems which cannot be helped but we can make it so that families in Malawi don't have to depend on the weather for food or money and have a variety of foods available to them as we have in developing countries.

Martin Luther King made the point in his famous speech entitled 'I Have a Dream' that all men should be treated equally. All people are created equal so why shouldn't they be treated

equally? I have a dream too. A dream that consists of people sharing, not being greedy and people being generous in order to
achieve the goal of equality instead of there being two extremes.
Let everyone have a sufficient amount of food so that eventually
the words developing world will not exist anymore.

Máirín Ní Chonceannáin

*Gairmscoil Eínne, Aran Islands, County Galway,
Ireland, Age 12*

LIVING ON LESS THAN $2 A DAY IN THE DEVELOPING WORLD

When I arrived in Sudan on assignment for *The Irish Times*, I'm
not ashamed to say that the heat killed me. I'd drunk my water on
the plane and it didn't look like I'd find any here. In search of
clean water, I found a man named Aabideen. I looked him up and
down before I asked him for water. He wore bright clothing,
though they were nothing more than clean rags and black sandals.
He was a very kind man who lived with his wife Saadiya, her
brother Da'i, her father Daneesh, their three children and his
mother, Gaeti. I wasn't surprised when he told me this because I'd
heard that Sudanese families usually accommodated many family
members. He also didn't hesitate to answer any questions I asked.
'My wife and I love everyone very much but it's a struggle. We
have to work very hard to keep enough food on the table and our
children in school. Saadiya and I work twelve hours a day, as do
the kids. They don't mind the extra seven hours a day but it's
tough on them. Apart from school-work they care for the animals
and water the crops. Da'i also helps Saadiya with the cooking and
carrying the water while I am lucky enough to have a job here at

Juba Airport. It's only four hours a day earning me $6 a week. It's hard to live like this but we like it.'

... People said that if you asked a favour of your neighbour they'd be likely to grant it. I think it's because at some point or another, all Sudanese have had their fair share of problems. They understand that without help you or your family could come to serious harm. After gathering all the information needed, I decided to head back to Aabideen. I thought about what people had told me and wondered how far from home the average person would have to travel to get to the market to sell/trade/buy their goods. I figured I'd ask Aabideen when we got back to Juba Airport. He was waiting outside for us and said the average person in Sudan travels an hour to get to work, some even further. He gave the driver directions and we finally arrived at his hut. It was around four yards wide and five yards long. I briefly met Saadiya before I offered to help with carrying the water. She warned me it was a hard job but agreed.

Caring for the crops and carrying water back to the house is hard work. I'd only been carrying water for two hours when my legs gave out, but I caught the bucket. Aabideen was behind me laughing silently, I laughed, too. When we got back we boiled the water on the open fire.

... Saadiya and Da'i were cooking beans. The Sudanese rarely eat meat and rely on beans for protein. They drink camel's milk. They made extra beans for me. I told them it wasn't necessary, that I would get some in Bor but they insisted. I was starving so I ate, and ate, and ate! I couldn't resist – it was delicious and I had goat's milk instead of camel's. After dinner, we were joined by Sheena, a lady from far away town called Rumbek. Sheena said to me, 'Education here is terrible. My husband Heru-sha can't read or write. I'm signing up for the teacher's job since I'm educated. My children will go to school as long as they live under our roof.

We'll trade goods to get the fees because that's what you do here.' It must be difficult, I thought. We have to help...

Jolene Sysak

St. Vincent Ferrer High School, New York, USA, Age 14

THE FUTURE OF A CHILD BORN TODAY IN THE DEVELOPING WORLD

... Truthfully, in our nation today, most of the worries of an average child are spent over material objects such as trying to convince their parents to purchase a new laptop or a 3D television! We don't have to stress over the possibility of catching malaria, or wonder about the next time a meal will be served to us. Sadly, millions of children in developing countries around the world don't have our advantages. For them, it is an everyday struggle. It is their reality.

... Children like Naomi are out there, waiting to be given a chance. And we can give it to them! Each one of us doesn't have to be CNN's 'Hero of the Year' and save millions of lives, we only need to change ONE. Those children are our future. That one child we help might find a cure for cancer, end world hunger, or bring world peace. Now, that would be a terrible opportunity to pass up! We must act now. Every day about 25,000 children will die. That's about one death every three seconds. To deny helping our mankind would be an act of cowardice!

Albert Pine, a writer and military officer, once wrote, 'What we do for ourselves dies with us. What we do for others and the world remains and is immortal.'

John Baxter

Christian Brothers Grammar School, Omagh, Northern Ireland, Age 15

THE FUTURE OF A CHILD BORN TODAY IN THE DEVELOPING
WORLD

… It is tragic to think that somewhere in Bolivia, in a dark empty street with the smell of rot and decay hanging in the air, a young girl, less than fifteen, has given birth to a child that will never grow up. He may already be brain damaged but that does not matter to his mother. She will wrap him in rags and care for him, but that will not keep him fed, that will not give him an education and it may not even keep him alive.

To be at home now, sitting at my own desk, in my own room, in my warm house, with my parents and my luxuries, I can't believe how privileged I am. How lucky I am to have been born here and how insignificant my daily worries are.

Not everything about my trip to Bolivia was bad. I met some amazing people, some of whom may no longer be with us. The most amazing thing was that the children could play and laugh and dance and sing. These children have faced the worst that life can throw at them and yet they can smile.

When I think about Bolivia the phrase 'out of sight, out of mind' seemed fitting to describe the shanty town from the point of view of the people of La Paz. But upon thinking this through it is clearly not true. The shanty town may be out of mind but it is not out of sight. When watching the people exit the luxurious department stores you can see the look on their face. See their noses turn up. They have seen the shanty town, and they do not like it.

Clearly this is a place that is seen but is shunted to the back of the minds of the people in La Paz.

Mary Burns

Mercy Convent, Tuam, County Galway, Ireland, Age 15

LIVING ON LESS THAN $2 A DAY IN THE DEVELOPING WORLD

There are approximately 1.1 billion people living in India, and before arrival I had researched that 80% of these live on less than two dollars a day, meaning that about one-third of the world's poor live here. Two dollars a day, even less value than my native two euro, for daily food, shelter, clothing. I wondered, how do these people even survive? Those that do survive that is. There are high rates of illiteracy and anaemia, and most Indians are members of marginalized communities such as scheduled tribes and Muslims, and, as we know, Muslims are amongst the poorest in the world.

These people, they get up at sunrise, cook, work, and clean beyond their abilities, they look after their large families, in other words their insurance policy, with less than two dollars a day. If an average Irish person was challenged to survive on the equivalent of two dollars a day, they would fail miserably, because as Irish people they have been brought up to think money is plentiful, they'll always have a home, they'll always have food. The average Irish person would find this impossible. They spend money carelessly, on impulse buying, beauty therapy, home appliances, while the native people of India, of Bihar, live on less than two dollars for the day. They probably don't have a home, life or health insurance, they probably don't even have enough food to eat. It is this type of undernourishment that cause the people of India to develop diseases such anaemia and full out starvation. To bring a child into this world, of living on less than two dollars a day, would be torture for a young Indian mother, who would be unable to look after and care for her newborn child. Imagine sending your starving child to work, or school, as they complain about hunger, and you couldn't help them. You couldn't tell them you'll have dinner ready for them when they come home, you couldn't tell them that you'll give them a treat if they do something nice, you couldn't tell them because you couldn't do any of these things. With two dollars a day, most people would be lucky to pay their rent, if they even have a home, and a third of the eighty per cent sometimes do not even have the two dollars others have.

So, as a journalist of an internationally renowned newspaper, I plead with you, the people of Europe, to help these developing countries develop. If you think you don't have the time to help, Concern Worldwide is just a phone call away, and by doing this you can help significantly to improve the conditions of other human beings around the world, reducing poverty and disease everywhere. I hope that you will consider that if everyone thinks 'somebody else will do it', that nobody will do it. These people need our help, and Concern are here to help us give it to them.

Úna O'Brien

Loreto Secondary School, Fermoy, County Cork, Ireland, Age 13

THE FUTURE OF A CHILD BORN TODAY IN THE DEVELOPING WORLD

...If Asha lives until the age of five, a decision will have to be made. That decision is whether or not she can attend school and receive an education. Luckily, the local school gives free education, but whether she goes or not will depend on how much work needs to be done at home. However if she does start school, she may drop out before she reaches secondary level. We in the developed world take education for granted. Just stop and think what would you do without an education? Then there are children who complain about schoolwork or homework, whereas a child from the developing world would do anything for that opportunity.

As Asha becomes older, she will have to realise the seriousness of her life. She will have to realise how much her parents work and how much she will have to work just to have a dinner on the table or a roof over her head. When Asha grows up and has her own children, she will have have to go through the same challenges her mother has gone through. If Asha happens to get an education along with her family, I would hope she gets a good job but it seems like fantasy.

... Overall, the chances of Asha having a good stress-free life are growing smaller and smaller. You have just read some of the possibilities of what Asha's life may come to, but we don't know for sure what could happen to her. But what we do know is that it is not going to be pleasant.

Elaine Keane

Loreto Secondary School, Fermoy, County Cork, Ireland, Age 13

THE FUTURE OF A CHILD BORN TODAY IN THE DEVELOPING WORLD

... On her way home from school Hadiya walks an extra two miles out of her way with a giant pot to fill with water. Her mother makes this journey two times each day despite being pregnant. I went with Hadiya and Neema one day and it was torture! The pots were very heavy and it was such a long journey. My arms and legs were aching by the end of it. However I knew no matter how bad the pain was that it was worth it to have clean water to drink. More than one billion people in the world do not have access to clean water. I made the long journey twice a day with Neema and the more I did it the more I made the journey the less I ached. I even made the journey by myself a few times when Neema was approaching her due date. To give Kato, Neema and Hadiya clean water every day made me feel amazing – 43% of children in Africa do not have access to safe, accessible drinking water. I'm glad that Hadiya is not one of them.

It was times like these I wished I had brought more money with me. I had fed Kato and his family for the first few weeks after my arrival but I ran out of money quickly enough. I had earned my keep by doing chores around the house. I felt I should be doing more though. More than 40 per cent of Africans are suffering from long-term malnourishment and micro-nutrient deficiency. Kato, Neema, Hadiya and I never went without food but the food we had wasn't enough especially for a young girl and a pregnant woman. Nearly one-third of children in Africa are underweight.

... This family has gone through a lot but this baby was the light at the end of the tunnel. Tears of joy streamed down Hadiya's face when she saw her baby brother. A giant grin was on his face as Kato held his son up with great pride. I felt tears in my eyes. 'What does Asante's name mean?' I asked. 'Thank you,' Hadiya answered.

What did the future hold for Asante? Would he get an education? Would he go hungry? Would he have clean water? No one can answer these questions. Just looking at Asante I could tell he would be okay.

Caitrin Melon

St. Ciaran's College, Balleygawley, Northern Ireland, Age 12

LIVING ON LESS THAN $2 A DAY IN THE DEVELOPING WORLD

... It is difficult to put into words the horrors I see, from the mud huts to the dirty water and sewage. The mud huts are extremely small inside, usually only housing an open fire, a huge cauldron, and two buckets for fetching the dirty water. Three or four small bowls and a couple of spoons are all the utensils available for eating. It would be unthinkable for someone from the developed world to live in appalling conditions like these. Yet we expect our fellow humans to live this. What does this say about us?

The water comes from lakes and streams, however by the time it reaches these people it bears a closer resemblance to the sewage it has been contaminated by rather than anything fit for human consumption. It is no wonder these people have such a short life expectancy.

My experience in Kitwe has been very emotional, inspiring and heartening. The way people here live is just astounding. Meeting brave people like this has been simply overwhelming. When I go back to Ireland I will be grateful for what I have. I am certain that I will never forget the experience I have had with Tiwa, Tbasi, Mhina and Abasi. It has been the most encouraging adventure I have ever been on!

Rachel McGlinchey

Finn Valley College, Stranorlar, Lifford, County Donegal, Age 15

IMAGING THE FUTURE OF A CHILD BORN TODAY IN THE DEVELOPING WORLD

… As I sit here now, beside Jana in her freshly woven basket, her deep brown eyes twinkling with delight, her loving family surround her. All clueless toward the fate which may await them, I feel like an outsider. Here are eight of the nicest people I know, living in a cramped one bedroom hut in one of the most poverty-stricken areas of Africa. My stay here has now come to an end, and, as I walk to my taxi at the end of the road, I take one final look back at the family who have so graciously welcomed me into their home. They are all smiling and waving. I see Fatima in the middle, a red scarf tied over her head, surrounded by all her children. There was Aziz, towering over everyone else, the twins, Sara and Hala, hand-in-hand. Then there was Tareq, holding baby Jana, Omar, his wild hair making him easily distinguishable, and little Shayma, in her brother Aziz's arms, waving frantically. It hurt me to leave them, but I hope that, on my return to the office in Nairobi, I will be able to raise awareness of poverty in Africa. It has truthfully been one of the most eye-opening experiences of my life, and I will never forget it.

Poverty is a dreadful thing, which kills millions of children every year. I can still picture little Jana, sleeping soundly in her basket, hoping, praying that this fate doesn't await her.

Jean Langford

Gaelcoláiste Luimnigh, Limerick, Ireland, Age 15

LESSONS WE CAN LEARN FROM THE DEVELOPING WORLD

... So far the lessons I have laid down have been mainly about what I have that people in the developing world don't. They appreciate it when I don't. A lesson that we can all learn from the developing world is to stop taking our luxuries, loves and loved ones for granted. Should any of these factors be taken away from these lives I think we'd kick ourselves to death wondering, why didn't we appreciate them while we had the opportunity?

What our wealth gives us – even if we don't see ourselves as wealthy – is a greater range of choices. The poorer you are, the more limited are the possibilities open to you. This is true from the smallest matter of choosing whether or not you will have a snack or a cup of coffee right up to major life choices such as what school or college you will attend, or even if you will have a school you can attend. The wealth of the first world gives us daily privileges beyond anything imaginable to someone living in the desperate poverty of the third world. We choose on a daily basis how much we will eat or drink, how far we will travel, how much work we will do, and when we will sleep. We choose whether we will have large or small families, where we will live, and even how long we might live. These choices are the blessings granted by the wealth that surrounds us.

We should count our blessings. That is the biggest lesson we can learn from the developing world.

Leah Geoghegan

St. Joseph's Secondary School, Abbeyfeale, County Limerick, Age 15

LIVING ON LESS THAN $2 A DAY IN THE DEVELOPING WORLD

I am just a reporter, doing my job, reporting on what happens in the world but it is also my job to enlighten people. We have to realise that there are many lessons we can learn in life but one of the most important ones is that we are one world, all brothers and sisters. Some of us are lucky, some of us are not. It's our choice to help make the world a better place and learn that god made us all equal for a reason. No one is superior, whether it's to do with age, race and nationality or whether you have money or not. I am only a reporter, reporting on what is right in front of me. I am only one person, but together we are a community of brothers and sisters. It's up to you whether you turn the next page of this newspaper and forget all about this article, but no matter how many pages you turn, or newspapers you throw into the bin, poverty isn't something that can be gotten rid of that easily. You can't just forget about it and hope for the best. Poverty is always going to be there whether you try and forget about it or not.

Think of all the helpless people who have died in third world countries, the amount of lives that have been lost because we weren't trying hard enough to help out these people. There are many self-less, generous charities out there trying to offer their support and care for other people but they need our help. Let us help our brothers and sisters stay alive. I know my family are safe from starvation tonight, but my neighbours aren't.

Part Two

SENIOR CATEGORY

(16–18 years old)

FIRST PLACE – SENIOR

Louise Burke

Ursuline Secondary School, Thurles,
County Tipperary, Ireland, Age 17

THE FUTURE OF A CHILD BORN TODAY
IN THE DEVELOPING WORLD

A new day is dawning in Calcutta, the capital city of West Bengal, a north-western state of India. This day marks the start of new beginnings, new opportunities and most importantly, new life. For today I am visiting the Kumar family as they celebrate the birth of their sixth child. This baby girl was born only last night, and you would expect that I am visiting the family in the maternity ward of their local hospital. However the Kumar family are at home. They never went to a hospital, mainly because they don't have one. There was no doctor present to deliver the baby because one was not available. The little girl won't receive any vaccinations as the family cannot afford them. The Kumar family are street dwellers, who live in one of the many shanty towns surrounding Calcutta. They are poverty stricken.

As I approach their 'home' I am shocked to see what life in the slums or *bustees* is like. People live in primitive, hastily constructed huts made out of clay, wattle, timber and galvanised iron. The winding dirt trail to the Kumar house is littered with rubbish. The smell is repugnant and I can only attribute this to the fact that rubbish is rarely collected here and indoor plumbing is no more than a dream to many of the inhabitants. As the sun shines down upon me I imagine if the little Kumar girl will one day run through these streets with her siblings. Maybe they'll find a football or maybe the large discarded pieces of timber and metal that I view as rubbish, will provide for them a playground, a hideout, ideal for hide and seek. They say one man's trash is another man's treasure! My thoughts are cut short when I realise I've reached my destination.

To some, the house would appear as no more than dilapidated. However as it comes into view I cannot help but smile. A sense of warmth and happiness is radiated from it. The bright blue front door is only propped up against the wall. I assume it will stay that way for the day as a stream of well-wishing neighbours trickles in and out of the house. Mr. Kumar catches sight of me and instantly rushes forward to greet me. He leads me inside while gushing about his new baby girl. They've decided to call her Sasmita, which means smiling.

We enter straight into the main living room of the house. It is evident that Sasmita is true to her name as everyone's faces are beaming despite their bleak and dreary surroundings. The room is dimly lit and overcrowded with people. On one side are the family's cooking utensils, a small amount of food and a space for a fire to be lit. The rest of the room contains a couple of broken chairs and a pile of dirty multi-coloured rags that, Mr. Kumar informs me, are waiting to be washed in the river by his eldest daughter Amira. One day, Sasmita will follow in her sister's footsteps. Her time will be divided between chores, work and if she's lucky some form of an education.

From as young as three years old Sasmita will be forced to help her family in whatever ways she can. This pressure will not come as laziness or cruelty on the part of her parents, but as a necessity for her to live. There is no running water in her home so Sasmita will have to help her siblings wash clothes in the river and also bring home drinking water. Life will be hard for this little girl. Washing her clothes and herself in the water she will later have to drink will leave Sasmita susceptible to diseases like typhoid and cholera.

As she gets older her parents can look forward to her first steps, her first word and her first job. Yesterday I accompanied her brother Hassan to the local dump, where he is paid to collect old batteries, rags and metal pipes. We set out at dawn as Hassan informed me it was too difficult to work in the afternoon. Then, the heat is too intense, the smell over-powering and the rats rule the land. I enjoyed my walk with Hassan. The clear, blue Indian sky was only just beginning to brighten. The dump was located on the far side of a steep hill. As we reached the top, the view that greeted me took my breath away, for more reasons than one. The sun was rising in the east and the morning sky was filled with brushstrokes of vivacious reds, illuminating oranges and warm yellows. However as the initial delight of this wore off I realised what lay beneath that sky. And I grasped that what I was actually looking at was a beautiful horror. Sprawling before my eyes was the dump. As expected, it was filled with bags of waste, broken furniture and shards of glass and metal. I was unprepared for the sight of dozens of children digging and clawing through the filth in search of items they could sell. Most of them were no more than six or seven and many of them were barefoot. Their hands were bloody and their eyes watered with the strain of trying to spot something of value. Hassan hurried in and got straight to work.

Was this what every child was reduced to in the slums? No, only the lucky ones. Many were sold into slavery or child prostitution. At least Hassan, Sasmita and their siblings had a home to go to after this. There are roughly 100,000 street children orphaned, lost or abandoned in Calcutta. Sasmita at the very least has a kind, loving family.

Upon my visit to their home her parents have much to say about their new baby girl. They are devastated and disappointed that they have no more than love to offer Sasmita. It breaks their hearts to think that one day she too will come home exhausted, aching and hungry and she won't have enough to eat. However they are determined that she will get an education, even if this only means enrolling her into evening classes after work. In a class of fifty she will need to be incredibly self-motivated if she is to learn to read and write. It is at this point her father asks me if I'd like to meet the little girl I'm making all this fuss about. He leads me to their bedroom where his wife is holding the baby in her arms. I'm overcome with emotion as I stare into that innocent child's eyes. They're big, bright and smiling- a shining light for the future. She may have been born in a small mud hut, in an under privileged part of the world, to poverty stricken parents, but that child is the most beautiful baby I've ever seen. This beauty spreads into all around her and right now her parents look like the richest people in the world.

So I end this article with a wish and a prayer, that the smiling light in that little girl's eyes will never fade, that her life will be filled with love and not hatred, happiness and not sorrow, good health and not disease, education and not child labour and finally kindness and not disregard. It is a simple wish that all children deserve, but unfortunately for Sasmita and other children in the developing world, a wish that is unlikely to become a reality without worldwide change, commitment and co-operation.

SECOND PLACE – SENIOR

Ciara Scanlan

*Ard Scoil na nDéise, Dungarvan,
County Waterford, Ireland, Age 16*

THE FUTURE OF A CHILD BORN
TODAY IN THE DEVELOPING WORLD

Fear is a distressing emotion aroused by impending danger, evil, pain or hazard whether the threat is real or imagined. In the developed world people commonly 'fear' needles, dentists and water. Sadly these are commodities that children in the developing world will never experience. These children have real fears. They fear death. They fear abduction. They fear rape. They fear to cry. I have witnessed these fears first hand. Being here in Gulu, Uganda, I look around only to see children with potbellies children who have been abandoned, children who fear.

On arrival, I was briefed about the Lord Resistance Army and I was warned about the danger I was putting myself in. I didn't care; I wanted to give the children of Gulu a voice. The whole international community has neglected these children. I have failed to find another country in the world having an emergency as colossal as Uganda, which has received so little media coverage. The world may choose to be ignorant but I won't be.

I find it difficult to understand the catalyst to this seventeen-year war but I gather that it began with a woman called Alice Lakwena. She is said to have been possessed by a spirit and attempted to overthrow the Ugandan government. She was brutally murdered but the war rages on. After her death a man named Joseph claimed to be her nephew. He abducts children to continue his war of madness. Once they have been taken into the bush, he desensitizes them and teaches them to kill. The LRA abduct children, who are 'mouldable', the easiest to manipulate and brainwash into being a soldier and killing innocent civilians. In this regard a child of five to seven years is the perfect candidate. They are big enough to carry guns yet small enough to sneak into schools and hospitals to snatch new recruits. Horror and fear are pushed into these minors. They fear to escape and instead withstand the torture and harassment. Over 50,000 abductions have been recorded since this war began but this number is not accurate, as many children are not listed on the live register. No one voluntarily joins the LRA yet it has a force of over 4,000. Is this a life that you would like for your child? This is the bleak future for thousands of Ugandan children. Yet it is ignored.

Children commute into town at night to sleep on verandas or at the bus shelter. These children fear sleeping in their own home. I arrived at the shelter one night to the sound of children, thousands and thousands of children. I was appalled to find no adult in sight except for a man with an AK47 strapped to his back and a can of beer in his hand. This is their only sanctuary. These children are hungry, these children are hurting, these children are frightened.

At the hospital where I am staying I met a group of young boys living beneath me in a dark and gloomy corridor. At night these boys would sneak away from the crowd of other children and sleep there even when the ground was soaking wet. Using whatever they can find, they mop up the puddles that are sometimes knee deep and then set up for the night. 'We used to go out to the forest and eat mangoes without fearing the rebels because in the day we cannot fear but in the night we can fear. At night we can fear those rebels, for me also, I fear to sleep at home.' Boni explains his situation to me and I can tell by his facial expressions that he is terrified. He is constantly frightened and he has left

86

traumatized by the abduction of his best friend. However, these children do not sit around moping, they take responsibility. These kids wake themselves up before dawn every day. They are under no constraint of parents or teachers requiring them to do so. Most of these children have lost their family because of aids and the LRA but they have become united and have created their own family. What does their future hold? Fear, danger, poverty.

I have noticed an evident difference between the emotions of Irish children and the children here in Gulu. The children here never cry. The children here are afraid to cry. They are afraid that if a soldier sees them crying that they will kill them. This is not how a child should feel. A child should feel secure and safe not insecure and anxious. When an Irish mother sends her child to school she expects that child to be looked after and safe. Two weeks ago a school, about two kilometres outside of Gulu, was ambushed. Forty-two children were abducted and fifteen others inhumanely murdered. If this were to happen in Ireland the story would hit global headlines. Why can't the same be said for Uganda? The children in Uganda are the same beings as the children in Ireland, America, China. Unfortunately, they were not born into wealth. Unfortunately, they were born into war. Unfortunately, they are treated like an overpopulated species of animals. Unfortunately no one cares. These children have needs. They need water, food, shelter and love. Yet their needs are not met. These children have dreams. They aspire to grow up to be teachers, lawyers, doctors. Yet these dreams will never come true. These children have wants. They all want peace. Is that too much to ask?

The future for the children of Gulu is bleak and dismal. Over 50% of adults in Gulu are psychologically disorientated. Imagine, you've been abducted as a child, you've been forced to torture and kill, you are a murderer. Traumatized is an understatement for the mental conditions of these people. Speaking to a girl called Fafa, I realized the full affects a life of fear and war can have on a child. 'I still get bad dreams and wake up screaming even when I am not sleeping I get bad dreams. I hear rebels threatening to kill me. I see a long line of children tied up in ropes. I see people's arms and legs being cut off. Children that were too weak to walk were chopped up and left to die'. At this moment, I realized how lucky I am. Not only do these children face a future of war. They also face a future of agony and little hope.

Without an end to this war in sight, these children somehow summon up the courage and faith to continue. That is why I return to Africa and will continue to return as long as my life will allow. There is a mind blowing hurt and fear here but at the same time an indescribable freedom and strength that will inspire me forever. As I pack my bags I remember the sight of the thousands of children in the bus shelter and think this wouldn't happen in Ireland. People may say that you cannot compare the two worlds. Why not?

THIRD PLACE – SENIOR

Katie Black

St. Paul's Secondary School,
Greenhills, Dublin, Ireland, Age 17

THE FUTURE OF A CHILD BORN
TODAY IN THE DEVELOPING WORLD

It's dark. Murky pools of light lie scattered around the floor. It is early morning, and the first shaky whispers of grey are beginning to reach into the dark night. There are sounds, hurried mutterings and footsteps issuing from one of the newly built temporary houses. I quicken my step, pass by identical building after building, their occupants silent from tireless labour. The sounds increase in volume and I see an anxious shape peer around the door, eyes squinted, and upon seeing me, beckon me eagerly to her side. A yellow glow washes over me and I see a stub of a candle leaning on the table. The room is small but clean. The candle is the only occupant of the table, a couple of chairs stand empty beside it and a cabinet with some plates takes up most of one wall. But the object of importance is the bed. There are about six people standing around it and I have to peer over their heads to get a view. Lying on the bed is a woman, and by her side, clutching her finger and looking straight at me with beautiful chocolate eyes lays a new born child.

It is January 11, 2011 on a mild morning in Haiti when this incident occurs. As I make my way back past the many houses, some completed and standing fresh and proud, many half naked, surrounded by ladders and tools, I can't help but wonder. I wonder about this child and what will become of it. It is one day from the year mark of the earthquake, which shook Haiti and the world on 12th January 2010. The tremors, which toppled down buildings and wrenched families apart, have stopped and retreated, having fulfilled their pointless duty. They have left much behind.

The ugly scars on Haiti's surface remain clear to this day; markers of the disaster can be seen at every corner. Buildings, from the most splendid cathedral to the humblest of huts, seem deserted. Tent cities have literally sprung up all over Port-au-Prince, thousands upon thousands of blue eyes blinking at the weary sun. The Haitians have become accustomed to the word 'temporary' – temporary shelter, temporary schools, temporary lives.

But as the sky shakes the stars from its inky cloak and the sun begins to peek through, I wonder how long temporary really is. Will this child, born tumbling into a stormy sea of confusion, ever know another way? Will this child's earliest memories be of hide-and-seek among the rubble?

And what of cholera, a disease that is claiming hundreds of thousands with its greedy fingers. With the highest mortality rate among children in the Western Hemisphere, one child out of every eight will probably die before the age of five in Haiti. At these odds, it's difficult to stay hopeful and if this child does manage to make it past the few early years, what next? Education is not easy to come by in Haiti. With the earthquake causing many schools to topple over like cardboard, and many families simply not being able to afford it, education is a luxury that lies out of reach for many Haitian children. Without access to even a basic education, Haiti's children are trapped in a cycle of poverty that has plagued the country for generations. If the children cannot bask in the glow of learning and so grab opportunities for themselves, will they ever truly emerge from the rubble?

Education is a stepping stone that I hope this child, in a few years' time, will be able to reach. If educated, this child could break a long line of poverty in a single family. However the road is long and strewn with obtrusions. It will take hard work, determination and a good handful of luck to bring the glow of education to this child's life.

As I think of the times ahead for this community, this family and this child, overall it seems to be bleak. One may ask why it is so; I find myself asking the same question. Money streams into Haiti on a daily basis. Rivers and floods of paper and metal come pouring in, but where does it go? This is a question many Haitians are asking themselves. This money, if used correctly, could shape landscapes, buildings and lives. If it could do all of that, then imagine what it could do to just one Haitian child. The tiniest sip of this sea of money could give this child the life that all Haitian parents would dream of for their child, healthy, educated and happy. That is all they wish.

These are not unreachable things. The future of this and all Haitian children born into this weary country is not set in stone. It is ever changing. However one thing is sure. And that is that change will not come over night. If this child is to have a chance at this tantalising future then this change has to be set in motion.

A few weeks ago the mother of this newborn child brought me somewhere. She didn't tell me where we were going. It was a beautiful day and the birds were singing in their makeshift nests among the makeshift homes. When we got to a clearing she took my hand and led me to a small object nestled amongst the hustle and bustle. As I got closer I saw that it was a cross, just a cross, a white, small and simple cross leaning on the dry earth. She told me that it was for her sister, who had been lost in the tremors. Then she smiled at me, a sad smile, and looked up at the sky.

In that moment I realised how she must feel – a cross for her sister. But does the future hold another cross, this time for her baby?

The road to a better future seems long, but as a Haitian proverb says, '*Chemen long pa touye moun*': 'A long road does not kill people'. This child has a chance. The day is still young.

SHORTLIST – SENIOR

Sarah Mabelson

Kilkenny College, Kilkenny, Ireland, Age 17

LIVING ON LESS THAN $2 A DAY IN THE DEVELOPING WORLD

It was a sweltering hot summer day, my tuk-tuk bumped along the orange dirt tracks deep in the West Nile region of Uganda. Warm dusty air blew on my face through the open window; it was thick with the spiced earth smell of Africa. I was on my way to visit the village where my driver, Ibrah, had grown up. Ibrah moved to Kampala aged 14 to find work. He recently told me he wanted to take me to see his real home and I eagerly obliged.

'The people of West Nile are poor, really poor,' he told me with rolling R's as we pulled into the village. He wasn't lying; Jagala, a small village near Jinja is made up of stereotypical round mud huts with straw roofs, set against a backdrop of dense green forest. A group of young children watched shyly by a chicken coop as I stiffly climbed out of the van. Ibrah's mother, 58-year-old Irene Mbabazo, greeted me. She wore a bright orange patterned dress and a brilliant white smile. As she lovingly embraced her son, her laughter was overflowing with soul. In her small hut Irene cooked us a generous meal of grilled maize, posho (a sticky plantain mash) and bean stew. We laughed as Ibrah recounted tales of his childhood and he translated our broken attempts at conversation.

In the fading afternoon Ibrah informed me that his mother was a talented seamstress. She blushed as she humbly produced her wares, brightly coloured bags covered in intricate beading. I was shocked, completely caught of guard by the beautiful craftsmanship before me, by the exquisite bags which would have looked more at home in a boutique in Covent Garden than in a small mud hut in rural Uganda.

When reflecting on my recent visit to Jagala I quickly became disgusted with myself. Why had I been so shocked by Irene's talent? It was because I had only been warned about the poverty of these people and I had never considered their talents. All I had heard of was their poverty so all I had expected was their poverty. I have been stationed in this beautiful country for over six months, yet I had still not managed to shake some of the prejudices that run so deep in Western culture today.

In the mainstream vein of journalism Africa is AIDS, starvation, mass rapes, blood diamonds, corrupted governments, child soldiers, machine guns and civil wars, relentless turmoil. All these horror stories form part of Africa, but to focus on them is to flatten our experience of the continent. As the Nigerian author Chimamanda Ndichi said, 'Show a people as one thing, only one thing, over and over again and that it what they become in our minds'. What if we stopped looking at this continent through pity tinted glasses? What could we learn?

Recently I spent an afternoon at Bombo Rd. Orphanage and Primary School in Kampala. At lunch break I found a very familiar scene: girls playing a skipping game, a young boy squealing as his friends tickled him on the ground. There were older boys climbing a jackfruit tree in search of its sickly sweet sticky prize, another group of them kicking a football around inside a giant cloud of orange dust. I joined one group of girls who were lost in an imaginary world, their only props six red straws and a three bottle caps. As one of them negotiated bargains in their 'shop' they had just as much fun as any Irish five-year-old playing with the latest 'Bratz' dolls.

It is often said that true joy in life cannot be bought or feigned, yet capitalism has taught us for so long that if we get the right numbers to go up life will be better. That more is better. The twinkle in Uganda's smile proves this is completely untrue.

Money does not mean happiness; it means survival, but we all know they are not the same thing. Studies have shown that, naturally, wealth improves happiness up to a certain level, to the level of survival. As soon as our basic physical needs are met our happiness is far greater influenced by our friends and family, by our sense of community than any material thing. As Robert Kennedy famously said, 'GDP measures everything except that which makes life worthwhile'. Our old financial paradigms have been shattered, yet if we can re-shift our values and look to the African joie de vivre in it is possible for us to be happier than ever before.

Time is another thing I believe we can learn a great deal about from the Ugandans. In the 'developed world' many of us start the day believing we are the lawful owners of the next 24 hours. This then leads to chronic impatience when we feel our time is being wasted or stolen from us by things we don't approve of, things we didn't plan for. The Ugandan view is quite different. Time is a gift. It washes over us. We can neither make more time nor retain one moment of it. Yet we often cling onto it so tightly, trying to stretch out our days with multitudes of 'time saving' devices. If our culture stopped seeing time as a commodity how many fewer people would die of stress-related illnesses each year?

When you think of Africa you don't usually associate it with mind-blowing innovation, but out of Malawi this month came a story far from the usual of hunger and despair. William Kamkwamba is from a family of rural farmers. When the crop failed he was 14 years old. He had to drop out of school, but that same year he built his family an electricity-generating windmill from spare parts he found at a scrap yard. He used a tractor fan, shock absorber, bicycle frame, PVC pipe (melted to make blades) and a bicycle dynamo. He worked from rough plans he found in a library book, following the diagrams, as he couldn't read the English. First the windmill powered one bulb in his small home then four with light switches. Now it also powers two radios and people are queuing up from miles around to charge their mobile phones.

In the face of failing crops and famine William refused to accept his future. Nobody told William it was impossible to build a windmill with no proper parts or electrical training, so he did it. He has plans to build another one to irrigate the land and defend his family against future famines like the one that destroyed his country.

Although Africa has many corrupt war criminals, it is also full of inspiring creative people like Irene and William. Although it has plenty of destructive barbaric traditions, it also has many cultural values that speak true to what is really important in life. There is so much we can learn from the rich facets of this beautiful continent if we come at it with the right frame of mind.

SHORTLIST – SENIOR

Hannah Gasset

Bellows Falls Union High School, Vermont, USA, Age 16

LIVING ON LESS THAN $2 A DAY IN THE DEVELOPING WORLD

How much do you make an hour? At the minimum you should be making at least eight dollars and working for around eight hours. So, before taxes you should be making $64 a day and if you worked seven days a week, it'd total about $448. Would you be able to support yourself and two children with three meals a day and a decent place to live with a weekly salary of $448? It would be difficult no doubt. Now imagine this same scenario, but earning 31 cents an hour, and about $2.48 for eight hours. Could you live on that? I'm sure you're thinking, 'Absolutely not!' Yet unfortunately, many people do. In India, the majority of the population, about 75% or 300 million people, is under the poverty line and makes less than two dollars a day. Also, they don't do eight hour shifts with mandatory breaks. Instead, many work 24-36 hour shifts, for less than a total of two dollars. That means each person is only making five to eight cents an hour. You may wonder how anyone could survive off that. Well, I had the opportunity to find out with an interview with Aamir Thakkar.*

As I walked down a back street in India to Aamir's home, in a place we would call 'slum', I began to really see the poverty and distress that Aamir and others like him have to live in. Makeshift huts and rundown buildings surround me. It had just rained, the road was filled with puddles; my shoes were soaked through, as there was little to no drainage system. Women and children stared at me from under water logged canopies. I felt out of place and guilty with my 'nice' clothes.

A young man approached me and through my translator introduced himself as Aamir Thakkar, the man I was looking for. He leads us to a small but well kept home; a little girl maybe four or five years old peeked out of the doorway. We walked into a dimly lit room, and Aamir motioned for us to sit on the mats on the floor. Sitting in a semi-circle, setting up for the interview I notice a young woman hold a little boy who is about two or three years old; I assume this woman is his wife and these two children are theirs. When we were comfortable and ready to start, the interview began.

Before starting with the questions, we asked Aamir to tell us about himself and his family. Aamir is twenty-seven, his wife is twenty-five, and his two children are five and two. He works for a full shift of twenty-four hours in a factory for an average of six cents an hour and then goes home to rest for six hours, then works for twelve hours at another job for only four cents an hour and then rests for another six hours before returning to his first job. We learn that Aamir was been polite enough to allow us to interview him during one of his six hour breaks that he usually uses to catch up on sleep. At the end of a full shift for both jobs, Aamir averages a total of a $1.92.

My first question for Aamir was, 'How does it make you feel, working for thirty-six hours and only making less than two dollars?' He looked slightly puzzled, but soon responded. 'This life is quite difficult, but all I've ever known. You ask how I feel, I must say I'm angered by how little we are paid. Yet, what can be done? Being paid little money is better than none. We cannot speak out, and I dare not quit my job, as I would be no better off anywhere else.' I then asked him how he and his family manage to eat three meals a day, afford a home, and purchase other household necessities? Aamir's immediate answer was, 'We don't eat three meals a day. Many times my wife and I skip meals so our children can eat. We go without materials we should have for our basic needs. Our rent is 'low', but still too high for us. Beds, proper clothing and filling meals would be a miracle and something we can only dream about.' During my visit I learned that Aamir's wife also works; she has a job at a day care center, so she can be with her children while earning money. Although both parents have careers, the pay is so minimal that their family expenses always exceed the money made from their jobs.

Aamir's interview about how his family somehow survives each day left me wondering why there are so many people being paid so little and governments and companies allowing it. There are many companies that have factories overseas in places such as India because they can pay the employees so little and give them no workers' or human rights. There are no required breaks, the working conditions are horrendous and the people must deal with it, as there is nowhere else they can go that will be any better. Companies such as Gap have written rules for worker's rights, but they claim that they can't enforce them overseas, and when inspections occur the employees are silenced by their superiors in fear of losing their jobs.

Knowing about men and women like Aamir cause us to realize how lucky and truly privileged we are. Living on two dollars a day is a challenge but they make it work, so why aren't we doing something to help them? Fight for workers' rights around the world and help others like Aamir and his family.

SHORTLIST – SENIOR

Elga Kursite

Banagher College, County Offaly, Ireland, Age 16

THE FUTURE OF A CHILD BORN TODAY IN THE DEVELOPING WORLD

How many times have you seen an advertisement on television with a little girl carrying heavy containers of water, or maybe a boy in a plantation doing a full adult's day of work, or a young mother struggling to find food for her newborn baby? How many times have you seen the captions 'a child dies every 3 seconds' or '215 million children are forced into child labour'? These stark statistics make us stop for a second, maybe look at our own children and thank God that they are healthy and educated and have a family that loves them. We know that our children will have a relatively secure future, in that they'll have a job, make money and lead a proper life. The reality is that those shocking images on those disturbing advertisements are only a tiny fraction of the horrifying lives children born in developing countries will lead. That is not to say, of course, that every child born in the Third World is going to have a terrible future, but the majority of children will be born into a vicious cycle encompassing a tragic mix of child labour, human trafficking, little or no education, poor health and grinding poverty. We can't even begin to imagine the lives they will lead.

A child that is born in a developing country is immediately at a disadvantage from the first gulp of air they take. In some cases, diseases such as HIV are passed on from the mother. The child is already born hungry because the mother was more than likely hungry herself. It's like laying the foundations of a building on a flood plain. The structure will already be in danger of collapsing before you even start to build it. The future of these kids is already bleak.

The baby is immediately exposed to life threatening illnesses – illnesses that tragically are completely curable in the developed world – such as measles, diarrhoea and the common cold. A lack of clean water and proper sewage systems also contribute to child deaths. An Ethiopian child is thirty times more likely to die by their fifth birthday than a child in the western-world. And the sad thing is that three quarters of these deaths are preventable. Research shows that these lives could be saved by low-tech, cost-effective measures such as vaccines and antibiotics. Those children who do survive and manage to make it past their fifth birthday now have to face other hardships that the future will bring.

The biggest issue after health in the developing world is education. It is a well known fact that a good education is the first step to a successful and happy life. Once a good strong foundation has been laid down, there will be fewer cracks in the walls of the building. But a large number of children growing up in the developing world won't even have the most basic reading, writing and mathematical skills. Millions of children don't attend primary schools and about twice the number don't attend secondary schools. Those children will grow up to make up the one in five adults in the developing world that cannot read or write. And what's even more disturbing is that girls are at an even bigger disadvantage when it comes to education since there are more illiterate females than males.

Children who don't get an education, be it because they're female or because they can't afford it, or both, really have no other choice but to work. 'Work' here does not mean a sixteen or seventeen year old getting a part-time job at the local shop down the road because they *want* (want, not need) more money to be able to go out with their friends at the weekend. No, 'work' here means a six or seven year old walking for miles to work full hours picking crops and carrying heavy loads to earn just two euro per day or less because they *need* it to survive. Unlike teenagers back home these kids have no choice but to work. They come from poor backgrounds with poor parents who send them to work because they either don't earn enough money or they can't work themselves because they suffer from long-term illnesses – a result of them working when they were young themselves. You can see clearly how big a problem child labour is. It's a vicious circle with no apparent end to it. Not receiving an education blocks the child's escape route from poverty. The progress in construction is brought to a standstill, and if the child is submitted to child labour it is likely to be abandoned altogether and the building will never be finished. Child labour stops the development of the child and significantly lowers the chances of it having a positive future.

One of the worst possible futures for a child is one in slavery. Slavery is the most horrendous, repulsive, appalling form of child labour. Thousands of children are trafficked every day to be used as slaves and are exploited in the most disgusting, disturbing ways imaginable.

Trafficked children are more prone to developing mental health problems, abusing drugs and alcohol and committing violent crimes in later life. Human trafficking not only puts a halt to the building but it tears it down, the child's progress in life is not only stopped but is reversed: their already poor quality of life is diminished further.

Another problem faced by children in the developing world is the violent environment they are forced to grow up in. Many nations in the Third World, especially in the continent of Africa, frequently suffer devastation brought about by warring tribes or rebel groups that oppose the government. Villages are ravaged, families are torn apart, and people's lives are destroyed. Over the last ten years two million children have been killed and another million orphaned.

One of the worst outcomes of these conflicts are the child soldiers. It is simply awful to think the only thing a child will be doing in the future is fighting and killing. Innocent little children as young as eight or younger are forced to handle weapons and kill other people. Children who are most at risk of becoming child soldiers are those who come from poor, disadvantaged families; others are kidnapped. It is estimated that over the last fifteen years ten thousand children were kidnapped by the Lord's Resistance Army in northern Uganda alone.

The concerns of a child in the developing world do not revolve around birthday parties or football matches or going out at the weekend. There is no guarantee of a healthy life, but there is hope for one. There is no guarantee that you will be educated and you will have a job, but there's hope that you will. There is no guarantee that you will not become a victim of violence and war, but there's hope that you won't. There's no guarantee that the building will be completed or that if it is, it will remain intact, but there's always hope. There's hope that in the future a deserted town can be built up into a city full of tall proud buildings, skyscrapers with bright shining lights beaming from every window. With help, there is hope.

SHORTLIST – SENIOR

Hazel Shaw

Kilkenny College, Kilkenny, Ireland, Age 17

THE FUTURE OF A CHILD BORN TODAY IN THE DEVELOPING WORLD

It's the 24th of January, and the sun is beating down on the bustling city of Kampala. The terra-cotta dust hangs in the air like an almost imperceptible fog, visible ripples of heat radiating off every surface. The drone of boda-bodas clattering down unlined roads, carrying loads twice their size, is constant. Women pass by carrying parcels of shopping on their heads as if they are weightless, and roadside stalls assail passers-by with new and improved 'best value' offers. Amidst the noises, smells and colours, amidst the chaos of this over-populated city, lies a new born infant. At this time one can only imagine what the future may hold for this child. A tiny and entirely innocent human being, thrust into a chaotic and disordered society. Yet who is to say that this isn't true of any child born today? Who is to say that this infant has a bleaker future than any other?

Having been stationed in Kampala, the capital city of Uganda for almost two years now, I have learned that although there is poverty, suffering and illness facing many of this country's population, there is an intense sense of community that has grown to override these day to day difficulties. The people I have met here are warm-hearted, kind and loving, and they show a great generosity of spirit. And if there was one place where I could say that I have felt this most, it would be here at the small school and children's home in the village of Jagla.

102

My first task here in Uganda was to come here to interview a woman by the name of Flavia Mbumbazi. My inevitable apprehensions of this first job were, however, immediately subsided by the young boy who came to greet me at the gate with a joy I had previously thought unimaginable. With the widest smile I had ever seen, he informed me that his name was Lawrence, and that it was great to see me.

During the hours I spent there that first afternoon, I got to know the inspirational story of Flavia's generosity. Flavia had always been a caring woman, and one day she simply decided to begin feeding children on the street from her modest home in Jagla. In her words, it was the least she could do. Due to the kindness of the society around her and the charity of humankind, her project flourished into a home for those children with no place else to go, as well as a school for their education.

This place has become a sanctuary for me, and over the years I have been introduced to all of the wonderful children here. I can honestly say that these are the friendliest children I have ever met, each of their faces glowing with a constant wide grin. These children, I quickly learned, are always eager to chat, and they have playfully nicknamed me Mzungu, which means 'white person'. Now I visit this sanctuary weekly, and even after two years, the whole-hearted joy with which I am welcomed is overwhelming.

I choose this place to write, as it is here that I find my inspiration. As I sit down to write this article, I hear in the background the gleeful, harmonious music of the children of the school, singing with joy their school anthem. 'We are the women, the men of Uganda, marching along the path of education. Singing and dancing with joy together, uniting for a better Uganda.'

It is this music that gives me hope, hope for the baby born today. You're right, we cannot be certain that this child's future will be bright and carefree, but I for one am certain that it is growing up in a caring society where it will learn the true value of life. Untainted by the greed for material goods, it will learn a faith that will endure through the hard times. I know that there could be no better role models for this child than the people surrounding me today.

When I think of my life back in Ireland, I am reminded of the obsession with wealth and celebrity culture, of a hierarchy based on possessions and earnings. And then I think of here, where people have learned to appreciate what they have by finding something much deeper than this. An inexplicable joy that I can barely understand is embedded in the hearts of the children I have met here.

So while we may know that developing countries suffer from many things that other countries were lucky enough to escape, what the western world doesn't know is that there is so much more to a developing world than poverty. What we must realise is that every society has its own difficulties to face, but these difficulties do not prevent the goodness in humanity from shining through.

It is for this reason that I hold on to hope, hope for the child born today. I have faith that this child's future will be bright. The children I have met over the last two years have founded this faith in me, and I will always have them to thank for that.

And so I urge you readers to grasp on to the same thing that I have, to believe in the strength of humanity through all things, to hope.

'Hope is the thing with feathers
That perches in the soul
And sings the tune without the words
And never stops – at all.'
– Emily Dickinson

SHORTLIST – SENIOR

Dara Griffen

Dominican College, Galway, Ireland, Age 16

THE FUTURE OF A CHILD BORN TODAY IN THE DEVELOPING WORLD

The town buzzed with late morning activity, women walking up and down the street with baskets on their heads, children running. One woman sat at the entrance to her shack, holding a baby tightly to her chest, talking in an unrecognisable language to another woman sitting next to her. They laughed heartily.

A pair of big brown eyes was watching us from behind the curtained entrance of a home. The girl couldn't have been more than eight years old, her skin mocha coloured and covered in a thin layer of dust. Her hair was wild, jet black and standing out at odd angles from her head.

We walked closer. Derek knelt down but the girl shrank back into the shadows. I put a hand on Derek's shoulder to restrain him, understanding how intimidating this big bearded giant must be. The girl watched us carefully, looking us up and down. She must have decided we were okay because she raised one long delicate finger. I followed her eyes to the camera hanging from Derek's neck. I smiled at her, pulling the camera over his head and holding it out to her. She took it into her hands, her fingers probing and prodding at the buttons.

A voice rang deep inside the shack and the girl turned quickly away, disappearing into the shadows. As we stood up a tall dark woman appeared at the curtain. She was at least a head taller than me, her chin held high. Her dark red dress was made of a wool fabric and her feet were bare. A baby slept comfortably against his mother's chest. 'Journalists?' she asked, her voice deep and her accent rolling the 'r'. 'Uh … yes,' Derek seemed to forget who he was by the sudden appearance of this elegant woman. I spoke over him: 'I believe we have an interview set up with you. I'm Bridget O'Connor and this is Derek Murphy, photographer.' 'Yes, come in,' the woman pulled back the curtain, gesturing inside.

It was a small single room that obviously served all purposes. There were mattresses and several blankets neatly stacked in a corner. An older woman stood by a fire, cooking something over the flames. Our young friend was standing in a corner. She raised the camera and clicked the button quickly, the flash illuminating the shack. The woman scolded the girl in a rough language and the girl lowered the camera. 'That's okay, she seems like a natural anyway,' Derek smiled at the girl encouragingly. 'In our culture, it is not appropriate for young ones to take without being given,' the woman replied. 'We did give it to her,' Derek answered, 'she can hold on to it for safe keeping.' The little girl smiled eagerly, snapping another picture of her grandmother at the fire before skipping out of the shack.

'Now, Ms Buhari, if we could start our interview,' I said, pulling out my paper and pen. 'Incidentally, what is your daughter's name?' 'Anika,' the woman replied, setting the baby down in a basket on the floor. 'She is seven next week.' 'That's a beautiful name,' I scribbled it down on my page, 'and her father?' 'Dead. He died of the sickness three years ago. It was very hard on us. The money ran out quickly. But I would not and I never will let my children work until they have an education. I took up two jobs, one working as a washer and the other as a harvester. It is hard work, but if it gets Anika her education, if it can make her something more, then I would take up twenty jobs. She's a very bright girl, Anika. She can multiply and divide and she can spell better than anyone else in her class. She told me last night she would like to be a scientist when she grows up.' A tear glistened in the woman's eye as she spoke.

As Anika's mother continued speaking I could see all her worldly possessions from my vantage point on the floor. It was hard to imagine anything further from the clinical world of science than this metal roofed, plastic walled home. But for this mother and her child the copy book and well-worn pencil carefully stored by the beds was the key to that world beyond the sand and heat. We continued the interview and when the time came to leave we walked back out into the hot street. Anika walked up to Derek, holding out the camera. It was still reasonably clean; she had obviously held it close so that the dust didn't stick to it. Derek took it back from her. She smiled and skipped back into the house without a word.

On the plane back to Dublin, Derek turned on the camera. The first picture was of Derek and I, both looking rather shocked by her surprise shot of us. The second was of the grandmother cooking over the fire. The third was of a little dog and a young boy. We flipped through the pictures, seeing Anika's world through her eyes. The final picture was of Anika herself, holding up her baby brother. She was smiling, and there was a glimmer of something in her eye I couldn't put my finger on. It was almost like hope.

SHORTLIST – SENIOR

Ciara Ansell

St. Wolstan's Community School, Kildare, Ireland, Age 16

THE FUTURE OF A CHILD BORN TODAY IN THE DEVELOPING WORLD

The developing world: a million miles away from us in the prosperous, western world and a million years behind our thriving and modern society. The problems in the developing world are so vast and so difficult to comprehend, that the majority of us just switch off. We turn of the devastating images on our television screens and we try to forget about the far distant problems that don't affect us. Dictators, starvation, disease, war, fear, poverty and famine all manage to build up to form an entire world in itself – the developing world. They are separate, distanced, and in so much trouble that they are quietly put away and boxed up where our moral values can't reach.

The act of boxing up these problems, problems that affect real people, real families, real children, has to end. So let's downsize the problems of the developing world and try to push away that dark, grey, swirling cloud that engulfs these devastatingly poor countries, masking their troubles. Let each problem get smaller and smaller and smaller until you simply have a baby. Imagine this newborn child, breathing its first hesitant breaths, unused to its new climate. Imagine its sharp cry as it moves away from the safety of its mother and in to the unknown, a place of endless possibilities and wonder. Imagine the hospital room, full of relief, of joy, and of love. See the balloons screaming in large, colour coded writing, what gender has just been born, the presents and cards littered across the bed. But stop. We are not in western civilisation anymore; anything that was normal to us has disappeared and we are in a new world too, we are in the developing world. A baby girl has just been born, frail and sick. This innocent child has arrived to a world she shouldn't have been brought to – a place of sadness, immense poverty and death.

The baby is born alive but she is hungry and weak. Her future looks bleak, uninviting, dark... Any light at the end of the tunnel, any deeply nestled hope for change, has been long extinguished. Death and poverty are not small problems that are being dealt with, they are monumental tidal waves that have taken over these people's lives for generations. Our young baby is in danger at every front. Virtually every global issue has targeted these countries and their civilians. Each seemingly un-solvable problem has weighed down on the people of the developing world so much that they now carry the weight of the world on their shoulders, barely surviving each day. Our baby girl has to face a million threats, disease, starvation, poverty, famine, war, death; and she is under 5. Everyone has the right to live, to dream, to love, to laugh without fear of death, oppression, or starvation, but these rights are not recognised in the developing world. In our civilisation we have painted a colourful world where we can reach the stars. However, we forgot to include the rest of the world and we have left them behind, dark, separate and colourless.

Our skinny, over-burdened child is one of the lucky ones and has lived past her fifth birthday. Although a child dies every three seconds due to extreme poverty and AIDS, she has survived. While our girl lives, her life is not at all easy. She is one of the 300 million children that go to bed hungry; she received no education and she works long hours at her local sweatshop. Her employers came from our world. They swooped down and took her life as their own. She works for them day in and day out for little money and no respect. She has no choice but to work for the dictators who employ her, they are her only lifeboat- the little she receives from them keeps her, just barely, afloat. She is dependent on them and will do anything to keep her job. With no money and no prospects our little girl is trapped in the strangling confines of her poverty stricken village.

Now she is an adolescent and she has HIV. Her world, already crashing around her, has been blown to pieces. Slowly, her immune system starts to fail; resulting in her frail body being susceptible to viruses and diseases. Her world, her country and her leaders have let her down and now, her own body has given up. Organs begin to shut down as her immune system is unable to fight back. Her sad life is drifting away from her and she is welcoming death, because with death comes peace and the end to her suffering, something that she has never experienced. She is gone; another person owing their death to AIDS, another funeral rite, another futile death. But her death, so far removed from the world and its conscience, has little effect on us. Her death was invisible and life goes on.

Life in the developing world continues, just as slowly and as grey as ever. People continue to die, sadness continues to occur, because we in the western don't have enough time to focus on a world of problems in a separate continent, and those in power in the developing world don't see problems. They don't see death or poverty or hardship. They are consumed with greed and selfishness, while their own people die around them desperate for freedom from their desolate lives. Their sole focus is money and power – so Africa stays behind them, dying a slow and painful death trying desperately to battle for its life. Life is not as it should be in these countries, and despots continue to rule despite their inhumanity and voracity. As one poor African man said, 'African Leaders . . . come as saints and leave as devils'. Our innocent baby girl had a short life, one plagued with pain and suffering, and lived in a world where the people in power ignored her.

How long do invisible deaths remain so? When does the revolution begin, where the developing world is looked straight in the eye by the western world? The blunt truth lies before you and the little girl we saw being born died after a tragically short life. Let's not let futile deaths continue. It's time to make a stand and recognise that we *can* make a difference, that the plague of hardship, famine, poverty, death, and disease has just found a cure – you. We need people who want this world to be a better place and who want every child to have equal rights. Let's help make the developing world a part of *The World*, so that every child born has hope, life, and rights, love, ambitions, dreams and happiness.

SHORTLIST – SENIOR

Selma Bouanane

Loreto Secondary School, Fermoy, County Cork Age 16

IMAGINING THE FUTURE OF A CHILD BORN TODAY IN THE DEVELOPING WORLD

From this land of gentle beauty, comes a story of terrifying brutality: Child soldiers. Some words just don't belong together …

He looks only ten, but the boy in baggy khaki uniform, eyeing us up suspiciously as we move through the village, represents one of the DR Congo's ugliest legacies: the use of child soldiers.

As a people, I think that it is fair to say that we have become desensitised to the hardships others must face every day. We are quite capable of eating our dinner while watching war-torn cities, strewn with corpses on the television. It is not that we don't care. At least, this is what I choose to believe. We are just so far removed from poverty and suffering, surrounded by our comforts and luxuries that we find it hard to perceive these horrific images as reality. How can it be, that in the twenty-first century poverty, misery and hunger still ravage entire nations of the Third World? As for the wars, I suppose there have always been wars. However, what is different about wars raging in countries such as the DR Congo is that they are fought with children. Children as young as seven are recruited into armed forces and are forced to become killers. In November 2010, I travelled to the Masisi district of the Democratic Republic of Congo to discover the horrifying truth behind the use of child soldiers...

The future for many children here is a bleak one. Innocent was born in Masisi, DR of Congo. He was born starving. Like millions of other children born in the Third World today, he will never receive a good education. Poverty will condemn his life to a gruelling existence of hunger and misery. Every day, he will have to fight for his right to exist. This is the beginning of every child's story here.

Three hundred pupils attend Masisi Community School. Despite the fact that these children walk to school with empty stomachs, their hearts are full of ambition and a burning hope of a better life ... a life devoid of hunger and poverty. Visiting a classroom, I asked a group of young boys about what they would like to become when they were older. They have dreams of becoming mechanics, engineers, football stars like David Beckham, though one hopes to become a pilot. The sad reality is that the chances of their dreams ever coming true are practically non-existent. Most of the children here drop out of school after third grade because their parents can no longer afford the fees. They turn to the streets looking for work, selling things like water and matches. Life on the streets is not easy. Children are constantly exposed to substance abuse, violence, sexually transmitted diseases ... it's an endless list. Others work in slums, searching for scraps they can sell on. Large machines drive in to deposit thousands of tonnes of rubbish. Sometimes, they don't see the little ones. However, the possibility of one horrific fate haunts every mother. The possibility that their child could be abducted into armed military forces.

Armed rebel groups, such as the Lord's Resistance Army (LRA), and some government military forces perceive children to be 'cheap' and 'expendable' recruits who can be easily intimidated and indoctrinated to commit atrocities, or even suicidal actions. A shortage of adults in protracted conflicts makes children even more vulnerable to recruitment. The proliferation of small, light arms, which can be easily handled by children also contributes to the problem. Children are frequently abducted from schools and refugee camps or coerced with promises of food or money. Some join to escape the relentless hardships of poverty and social discrimination. Most of the children who have swollen the ranks of the militia and the fragmented Congolese army have been abducted from their villages. Abductions are brutal, with many of the children witnessing family members and neighbours killed or the destruction of their homes, while some are forced to commit the atrocities themselves. The youngsters serve as front-line combatants, guards, porters, spies, messengers, servants and sexual slaves for armed government forces and rebel groups. Ngbendu was taken from his home when he was just 13 and forced to make a choice between the militia and death. 'When they came to my village, they asked my older brother whether he was ready to join the militia. He was just 17 and he said no; they shot him in the head. Then they asked me if I was ready to join up, what could I do? I didn't want to die.'

Child soldiers like Ngbendu encounter the extreme violence of modern warfare, the risk of injury, death, malnourishment and manipulation with drugs and alcohol. Girls, made to cook and carry heavy equipment, are particularly vulnerable to sexual exploitation, often resulting in infection with HIV/AIDS, ending up as 'soldier's wives', some as young as ten. Try to speak to them and they respond in monosyllabic hushed tones. These are

113

youngsters who have had their childhood innocence knocked out of them, quite literally.

Exposure to horrific violence, compounded by separation from family and social structures, has long-term consequences including substance addiction, physical disability and psychological trauma. Those child soldiers fortunate enough to survive a conflict or to escape face a long road of reintegration into normal community life. Many are desensitised to violence and have difficulty adapting to life without a weapon. They often face resentment from family and friends because of the horrific acts they have been forced to commit. Rehabilitating former child soldiers and assisting them to live as productive citizens is a difficult process. A third of DR Congo's child soldiers will never be reintegrated back into their communities, in some cases because of the shame, in others simply because their family can't afford to take them on, but also because of the ever-present threats and intimidations which hound ex-child soldiers attempting to reintegrate into their community. Unfortunately, this is the future of many a child born in the DR of Congo and many other Third World countries today.

I accompanied 12-year-old Etienne Kimba as he made his way back home. Etienne was a fighter battling against the Mai Mai militia. In his village, his mother and siblings embrace him with tears and cries of joy, but on the fringes of the celebrations the same militia that abducted him are looking on. In a part of DR Congo where virtually all Etienne's fellow children are severely malnourished and in tattered clothing, a life with the rebels offers food, power and some status. A sad reality is that all too often children like Etienne return.

For others like Wembe, another ex-child soldier, the future is a constant fear of re-abduction. Wembe was abducted by the LRA when he was 11 years old. At the age of thirteen, he managed to escape, however six month later he was found, arrested, beaten severely and forced to take up arms again. A month ago, he escaped. This time he came home to find his 10-year-old brother had recently been abducted. 'Every day my family and I hope that he will come home so that we can be reunited again.' In the meantime, Wembe lives every minute in fear of possible arrest and more serious torture.

The ongoing abduction, forced conscription, and killing of children in countries like DR Congo is perhaps the worst violation of children's rights anywhere in the world. There are currently an estimated 300,000 children engaged as soldiers in 30 countries worldwide. Some 120,000 children are fighting in Africa alone, with similar numbers in Asia and South America.

> 'Children are our future. To accept the use of child soldiers in conflict is to accept the destruction of our future, one child at a time.' – Kofi Annan, UN Special Session on Children, May 2002

A child crouches in the rubble. His eyes are wide with terror. A deep gash in his chest oozes blood. His trembling hands grasp the rifle. Squeezing his eyes shut, he presses the trigger. He hears the high-pitched screech of bullets as they pierce through the air, followed by a cry of pain, a heavy thud. A single tear rolls down his cheek. This could be your child. Take a stand.

PASSAGES – SENIOR

Helen Hildreth

Bellow Falls Union High School, Vermont, USA, Age 16

LIVING ON LESS THAN $2 A DAY IN THE DEVELOPING WORLD

… Bala Edha and her family are great people and struggle in the everyday life of Mumbai, India. People in the US struggle with homes and living situations but they get help. There are shelters with food, water, and lavatories. I think that there should be shelters in Mumbai and everywhere else. Imagine living in a slum and not having food or water for days and only making less than $2 a day. They don't get to eat three meals a day or take a shower whenever they want to. That is how Balas family lives on an everyday basis. I think that if people made an organization to raise money for the people of Mumbai we could help them out a lot. We could get them food, water, and clothes. People might think there isn't anything wrong with it when they see the beautiful city. But once you research and dig down deep to where people have nothing, it would really open your eyes. But always keep in mind that other people might be less fortunate than you, so maybe share with them or give them something that you don't use or want. It is a great way to make new friends. Keep Mumbai in mind.

Laura Scally

Tullamore College, County Offaly, Ireland, Age 17

LESSONS WE CAN LEARN FROM THE DEVELOPING WORLD

... Likewise, we take our education for granted. In any school in Ireland, and indeed in the Developed World, you will see students slugging into a classroom, wishing they were anywhere bar there, cursing their free education and pondering over why they should even turn up anymore. They'll throw their bag onto the desk in front of them and take out books, pens and copies, all while staring out the window beside them

Now take a look at a school in Africa. You'll see children smiling eagerly as they walk miles to school. Once they reach the building, most likely a shack, sometimes just an open space with not protection from the elements. That child will relish every moment in school, absorbing as much information as humanly possible while anticipating the moment that they'll get to use the pencil and practice their handwriting.

Staying in Africa we go home with that child and see how they interact with the whole community, greeting people as they pass, offering assistance. At night they may all gather around a communal fire, sharing food whilst singing and dancing.

... We often hear students proclaim themselves 'poor' with 'nothing to eat'. They wouldn't understand the real meaning of poverty and hunger. If you place a child from the Developing World in a student's house, they'll be more than flabbergasted. They'll open the fridge that has 'nothing' in it and see hordes of food. That piece of cheese, slice of ham and egg would be a feast! Rooting through presses the child will find loaves of bread, bags of pasta and rice, peas and carrots. The child would think of how long the food would feed their family, their own village even, and

117

we have the gall and cheek to say 'there's nothing in it,' simply because food is in abundance here...

Eimear Dunne

Scoil Bhride, Mercy Secondary School, Tuam, County Galway, Age 16

LIVING ON LESS THAN $2 A DAY IN THE DEVELOPING WORLD

One cup of Starbucks coffee, two chocolate bars, the income more than half of the world lives on – what could these three things possibly have in common? They are all equal to about two dollars. This may seem a little sensational to some, but living on the price of a cup of coffee is the stark daily reality for more than two and a half billion people worldwide. It's hard to imagine that once the bitter-sweet taste of your morning coffee has made your weary eyes just a little more alert, you've spent the average daily income of half the population of the world. Now that's a sobering fact.

Two dollars a day is the United Nation's current baseline definition of absolute poverty, which over two and a half billion people in the global south survive on. Where does this two dollars actually come from though? Are all poor people given two dollars a day to live on? The answer to the latter is obviously a no, which warrants other possibilities. There is little industry or manufacturing in most developing countries, so a job in a factory is out of the question for most. The answer I have found is, of course, that there is no simple answer as to where the money comes from. Two and a half billion people hardly have the same job, after all. Since finding myself stationed in the epicentre of absolute poverty, here in Uganda, I have made a few observations.

... Poverty often means not being able to take advantage of opportunities such as education. It is widely accepted that the best way out of poverty is to get a good education. Many families however, cannot afford to pay for school, or school supplies. Even with free schooling provided by aid agencies, families cannot afford to lose the income the child would generate working. Without any formal education, the poor are often confined to subsistence activities and low wage labour for years to come.

Brian Shaw

Coláiste Phobal, Roscrea, County Tipperary, Ireland, Age 18

LIVING ON LESS THAN $2 A DAY IN THE DEVELOPING WORLD

... The chances of a good job for Yana and Roger are slim to none. The economy of Uganda is one of the weakest in the world, with Idi Amin's vicious reign in the 1980s being a major reason. The average income is less than half of the sub-Saharan African average, which itself is way below the western world. The corruption is highlighted in the fact that, despite the economy growing in recent years, the poverty level has risen in those same years. The poorest, including Yana and Roger, are not benefiting from the stronger economy and this is grossly unfair. It's the opposite of the Robin Hood scenario – money is being taken from the poor and being given to the rich (the government officials). Chances are Roger will end up illegally in the forests like Yana's dad, due to the lack of opportunities for young people, while Yana will be forced to marry a stranger and provide him with all the pleasure he wants; a pointless and hopeless future for her.

I have been truly shocked and appalled while working here for the past few weeks, to an even greater extent than from my usual corruption reporting. Here, corruption is not just damaging people's lives, it's destroying them and shattering all hopes and dreams. Children like Yana and Roger have very little reason to be optimistic about the future but, I hope, with the help of charities and the international community, the situation will improve as soon as possible. I will certainly be doing my part as soon as my next payslip arrives at my desk in Frankfurt.

Lucy Butler

Presentation Secondary School, Clonmel, County Tipperary, Age 16

LIVING ON LESS THAN $2 A DAY IN THE DEVELOPING WORLD

... Imagine this shocking fact: the price of ONE missile could pay for school lunches for a school full of children for FIVE YEARS!!! People should stop fighting and act in a more selfless mature manner. It would save lives, money and time.

Imagine living a life of fear, sadness, hunger, illness and pain rather than the life of health, wealth and happiness that we live. It is by luck if you are born to a good life. Imagine if all the people in the developed countries got together to help improve the lives of those living in the developing world. This would bring every campaign for world peace into action. Imagine having the ability to change someone's life from misery to utter happiness by simply giving money, shelter and food.

Imagine you were born to a sad hungry maybe dying mother. Imagine the house you live in now was gone and you lived in a damp, cold, unstable shack. Imagine you and no food for days and your body started to break down. Imagine having no education and have no chance of a job or an opportunity to get out of poverty. Imagine having to engage in child labour to help feed your starving family. Imagine your family and friends are dying every day because of basic necessities like food and water.

Such is the life of a child born today in a developing country.

Niamh Fahy

St. Joseph of Cluny Secondary School, Killiney, County Dublin, Age 16

LESSONS WE CAN LEARN FROM THE DEVELOPING WORLD

'Third World' (noun) – the countries of the world that are outside the main industrial economies of Europe, America, Asia and Australia'. Pretty straightforward right? Not really. This is how 'Third World' was defined in the Heinemann English Dictionary, which is open on my lap.

I was asked by my editor to write around 1,000 words on important lessons we can learn from the developing world. But there are not enough words in the world to describe that. So I thought the dictionary would be a good place to start.

Now this isn't about how the dictionary defines the 'Third World' but how the world defines the third world. Third World, does this mean I live in the first or second world? Are countries simply ranked indifferently and so some countries are just not 'first class' and others are? This shouldn't be the way the world works. The world is the Earth, including all of its inhabitants and the things upon it. So the 'Third World' is 'supposedly' part of the earth but yet is considered and referred to as a completely different world, separate to the rest.

And yet this incredible, isolated 'world' can teach the 'first world' some of the most important lessons in life.

... We can learn from the third world; how to treat people, how to share, how to love, how to help everyone in the world so that the Earth and mankind needs not to be divided but rather connected. It may be tough and take time, but that's a small price to pay for something that would benefit the whole of humankind.

Ciaran Gaffney

Gaelcholáiste Luimnigh, Limerick, Ireland, Age 15

IMAGINING THE LIFE OF A CHILD BORN TODAY IN THE DEVELOPING WORLD

... I wasn't exactly taking in what was happening. I came here around three weeks ago to get a taste of India and the slums, poverty and squalor that some of Dharavi's residents live in, and a taste is certainly what I got. While all this commotion was taking place, I couldn't help but look at the oblivious little baby boy. Little did he know that his mother, the women who just brought him into the world died doing so, little did he know that he was going to grow up in a two room flat in a slum full of disease, sewage and pollution with a hole in the floor as a toilet, and rats and dangerous spiders and insects of all kinds creeping around the floor. The education in Dharavi is minimal. Kazuo's grandmother and aunts and uncles cannot read or write, and he will more than likely start working when he's ten at the latest. I wonder will he be treated the same way as the other children in his family, since his mother died giving birth to him. His grandmother, Jushti, quite a firm, unfriendly women showed no signs of joy when Kazuo was born. From having witnessed that, I have the most horrible feeling that she will not treat him any better as his mother died giving birth to him.

It is not my place to imagine a child's future, but this poor boy could be carrying any sort of disease, including cholera or the AIDS virus, as they are both very common diseases in these disgusting slums. The flat where Kazuo lives stinks of everything possible. This poverty stricken family have no money for any sort of luxury, not even a necessity. For instance, the Singh family don't have running water, the house is warm, there is dirt everywhere they sleep on mattresses which they found on the streets. They are poor, they have very little money, they live on €3 a day and that would be pushing it. I can only show empathy for this poor family, especially Kazuo, he has a long life ahead of him … or maybe he doesn't …

Emer Gerrard

Loreto Abbey Secondary School, Dalkey, County Dublin, Ireland, Age 17

IMAGINING THE FUTURE OF A CHILD BORN TODAY IN THE DEVELOPING WORLD

… Three years have passed. Now fifteen, Pharah is cleaning the small kitchen with her mother. In the corner of the room, a baby is sleeping quietly. This child has been brought to this world by our child, Pharah. Despite wishing the best for Pharah, her mother simply could not continue her daughter's education. She now flinches as she thinks about the days when all Pharah could talk about was where she would go when she was older, how she would live in a nice house with a nice man and be a lawyer. Pharah's mother also remembers with sadness the day her daughter came home to tell her she was pregnant, that she had been the victim of a crime that could never be talked about. Pharah's baby begins to cry. Wearily, Pharah walks over and picks him up. Pharah's mother watches painfully as a child, her child, feeds another.

With diligence and patience, Pharah and her mother rear the little boy. They watch him grow strong and kind, filled with the dreams Pharah herself once had. As he makes his way to school every day, Pharah, like her mother before her prays that her child will find happiness and hope in the world, that things will be better this time.

After saving carefully and securing a small loan from the bank, Pharah is able to send her thirteen year old son to a secondary school. When Pharah first tells her mother of this news, she sees an expression mixed with happiness and shame. Pharah's son works hard in his new school. Pharah hopes that this chance will prevent him getting involved with the horrible groups so many people's sons get drawn into. Perhaps the future will shine brighter for him.

During her son's eighteenth year, Pharah attends his graduation from secondary school. She smiles proudly as his name is called out. As she walks home from the school, linking her mother, she cannot help but feel giddy with joy at the news that her son will be moving to America due to a scholarship he has earned. It has been arranged for his mother and grandmother to come to America with him. Even though Pharah is only thirty-three she knows that she has felt like an old woman for years too long. Maybe now she will receive her chance at life, not in her own country, but one miles and dreams away. Maybe now she will see the future she always dreamed and imagined.

Aoife Ni Bhriain Ni Argain

Coláiste Ide, Dingle, County Kerry, Ireland, Age 16

IMAGINING THE LIFE OF A CHILD BORN TODAY IN THE
DEVELOPING WORLD

... Today, I am two days old. My Mommy is holding me in her arms and she is telling me about my 'room'. It is yellow and there is wood on the ground. She said there is a wooden crib with a nice soft mattress and warm blankets and that's where I will sleep. Daddy said he put in a nightlight so the dark won't scare me and he said that it will put nice pictures of Winnie the Pooh on the ceiling for me to watch and he said that he put a 'mobile' hanging off the ceiling with animals on it, I hope it doesn't hurt the animals. My room sounds really cool and Daddy said it's all mine. Mommy said its right next to her room so she can come to me quickly if I start crying. My Mommy and Daddy love me very much.

Today, I am two days old. My brothers and sisters are taking care of me today, but they don't really know what to do. I still have that bad pain in my stomach. Why won't they make it go away? I have three brothers and three sisters. My oldest brother is taking the most care of me. His name is Betserai, it means 'rescuer' because he said that Daddy told him he will have to take care of the family when Daddy no longer can. My oldest sister is named Dananai, it means 'love one another', she said that Mommy told her that she will have to do the cooking and cleaning and make sure she takes care and loves everyone when Mommy no longer can, and then she started crying ...

Today, I am three days old. My Mommy and Daddy are trying to pick a name for me. They have decided on Alexandra, it means 'Helper of Mankind'. Mommy told me that not everyone is as lucky as me and some people are born sick. I don't think that's fair, I'm going to fix that. I'll make sure that everyone is as lucky as me. Mommy and Daddy said I can do anything and that's what I'm going to do.

Today, I am three days old. Mommy is gone. I miss her very much. I thought she would always be there. I am very sick. Daddy thinks I have 'African Sleeping Sickness' because there is a big red bite mark on my leg and I'm very hot and it really hurts when I move so I cry. He looks worried, but he keeps saying, 'you'll be okay, Mommy is watching over you, her little baby girl, you'll be okay'. That pain is still in my stomach, it's after getting worse. Daddy picked my name today. He said Mommy picked it before she went to sleep and that she said she was sorry then he started crying again. My name is Chiramwiwa, it means 'abandoned'. What does abandoned mean?

Today, I am four days old. I am going home to start my life. I can't wait, it will be brilliant. Today, I am four days old. Today I died.

Lauren Dixon

Kalamalka Secondary School, British Columbia, Canada, Age 16

LIVING ON LESS THAT $2 A DAY IN THE DEVELOPING WORLD

... Across the hillside the cattle graze what is left of the scarce vegetation, barely surviving. Corn, rice, beans, otoe, bananas, mangos, oranges and nance struggle to flourish in the harsh growing conditions of the island. Crop yields decrease more and more each year. Even though men work day and night in the field, there is hardly an adequate amount of food cultivated for the people of Salt Creek and the workers are left exhausted and in dire need of medical care. Jorge, whose name translates to 'earth worker', is a farmer here. His calloused fingers are visible to the naked eye and his clothing is torn and smothered with soil. Jorge returns home dehydrated and frail with only a mouthful to show for his efforts. The daily life of this farmer in a village of only a few hundred runs parallel with almost every face around him. His reality is everyone's reality.

... It is Tuesday and instead of being at school, Ofelia (meaning 'the helper') is trekking through the mangroves as she does every day to collect water in the creek for her family. The water is hardly clear and evidently contaminated with raw sewage- but this is their only source. She cups her hands and scoops the contaminated water. She sips vigorously, quenching her thirst from the long journey. She then dips the basket into the creek, letting the water cascade inside. Once full, she places it above her forehead, maintains her balance and heads back towards Salt Creek. Ofelia struggles as she carries the water basket above her head, slipping through the viscous mud and climbing over tree roots. The umbrage surrounds her, as shadows chase the heels of her feet. The imprints in the rust coloured soil are imperfect as she rushes past the familiar. Ofelia passes the incline bordering the township and her toes touch the hand-laid brick path. She then feels safety enveloping her. As she reaches the precincts of her cane house, Ofelia places the deadweight of the water next to the fire. The open flame belches smoke, suffocating the one-room shack. She looks up and her father, Jorge, is home to have a sip of water. He smiles. This is only a stint in her day, it is only midday. The daily life of this girl in a village of only a few hundred runs parallel with almost every face around her. Her reality is everyone's reality.

Rebecca Toner

Our Lady's Grammar School, Newry, Northern Ireland, Age 18

THE FUTURE OF A CHILD BORN TODAY IN THE DEVELOPING WORLD

... Another basic need that we in the developed world find ourselves lost without is clean running water. Lack of clean water in the developed world kills 2 million children a year. Any water that would be available to those in a village of a developed country may be contaminated with sewage, leading to the spread of typhoid and the highly contagious cholera. River blindness is also caused by a parasite found in the water which enters the eye then washing. A total of 1.1 billion people have a lack of clean water, and 2.6 billion suffer from inadequate sewage. Even though the majority of us in the developed world have taps in every bath or kitchen with functional plumbing, those in the developed world consider having a well per village as a luxury. The fact is that citizens of many African countries receive less than 20 litres of water a day, as opposed to a British citizen who uses no less than 150 litres a day, while Americans use 600 litres a day.

A need that we certainly not only take for granted but often complain about is the chance to go to school and receive an education. Many children in the developing world rely on sponsorship for schooling. A third of people in the developing world are currently illiterate, and as of 2000 125 million children from 6-11 years old are not in school and receiving and education. Another big threat is that some countries do not believe in educating girls. It is often frowned upon in some third world countries when the girls go to school. Many of them will not go out of fear of retaliation or humiliation. This fear can often lead to violence when the

128

townsfolk seek some sort of revenge when the girls keep on attending school.

... The final basic need which should be available to all children is the opportunity to find work. Children born in the developing world today will become stuck in a poverty cycle as they receive a poor education, if any at all, and therefore can only be employed in low-paid jobs with little chance of making enough money to break out of the poverty cycle.

Blainaid Leonard-Moore

Largy College, Clones, County Monaghan, Age 16

LIVING ON LESS THAN $2 A DAY IN THE DEVELOPING WORLD

... Discussing the implications of Uganda's high population growth rate in Kampala, Prof. Augustus Nuwagaba, a poverty eradication expert, said while countries with high populations can benefit from a demographic dividend, 56 per cent of Uganda's population which is below 18 years old only spells disaster.

'The fast-increasing population appears to be the factor in the rising absolute number of people living in poverty. The current population growth rate is unsustainable because it's not producing a quality population. If such a population is not checked, it will only turn into a disaster,' Dr Nuwagaba said.

Therefore, to tackle this problem of poverty in the developing world, the rising population must be addressed. If these countries are unable to cope with their existing population figure, they are not going to cope with an even larger one. To mend the population crisis factor, education must be looked at first. Nearly a billion people entered the 21st century unable to read a book or sign their name. Contraceptive information must be available and accessable in order to both halt the population growth, and also tackle the problem of women dying during labour.

My experiences in Uganda – the insight I received in regards to the economic instability in the country, and the people I met – have carved a new path for me in life. I want to be able to look back in ten years and think 'Look at this booming Ugandan economy.' I want the hardships of living on less than $2 a day to be nothing more than a distant memory for the peoples of the developing world.

Aíné O'Connell

Loreto Secondary School, Balbriggan, County Dublin, Age 16

THE FUTURE OF A CHILD BORN TODAY IN THE DEVELOPING WORLD

A child born today in Ireland, a developed country, is faced with the issues of heavy tax rates, overcrowded classrooms and long waits in hospitals. While people say that our children's children will still be paying back the debt we have gotten ourselves into, is this really the worst situation we could be in? Children born to-day in the developing world are subject to much worse issues than these. There are wars happening, disease is prominent, most do not receive an education and thousands live in overcrowded shanty towns.

According to WHO (World Health Organisation), a child born today in a developed country is one hundred times more likely to die before it's fifth birthday than in Iceland, which has the lowest infant death rate in Europe. Many factors contribute to the reasons for this significant difference in child mortality. In the developed world, if a child is sick it is brought to its local general practise or hospital. If the parents cannot afford this, medical cards can be obtained to help them. While they may have to wait due to cut backs in the health system, if they are sick they will be seen to. In the developing world, however, workers are lucky to receive $2 a day, if they have a job at all. This tiny wage has to cover food, shelter, clothes and other such expenses. So, a trip to the doctor or hospital is not very likely to be affordable to the family. Besides the price though, not many general practises and hospitals exist in the developing world. Therefore it could be a long distance to the nearest one.

While people living in the developed world can often be heard complaining about overcrowded classrooms, they do not realise how lucky they are to have had an education at all. In the developing world ninety-three million children do not get an education. This can be due to the fact that they may have to stay at home and mind their younger siblings while their parents work, or they may have to work themselves. Child labour is common in developing countries. This would not be tolerated in any country in the developed world as there are child protection laws to prevent it. There is a minimum age of sixteen put in place as well as a minimum wage to stop businesses hiring children cheaply. However, in the developing world, no such laws exist ...

Rebecca Mulcahy

Presentation Secondary School, Cork, Ireland, Age 16

THE FUTURE OF A CHILD BORN TODAY IN THE DEVELOPING WORLD

... If we were to follow Alile's life it would, most likely, be full of tragedy and hardship. Seeing as in the third world there are 640 million children without adequate shelter (1 in 3), 400 million with no access to safe water (1 in 5) and 270 million with no access to health services (1 in 7), she would be extremely lucky to live past the age of 5.

If she were to live past this age she would most likely work on a tobacco farm harvesting tobacco leaves. If Alile were to continue doing this, she would not only miss out the chance to escape poverty through education, but she would also be putting herself at risk of green tobacco sickness. This is brought about by nicotine

132

absorption through the skin and results in severe headaches and a debilitating coughs, leading to chest problems. It seems that no matter what she does, poverty and disease are always around the corner. If she survives past this point she will most likely have a number of unplanned pregnancies, as 20% of births in Malawi are a result of unprotected sex.

Alile, whether she is a factual or fictitious character, is a prime example of a child living in an under-developed country, and shows how the majority of these children's lives will play out. Sadly, we have become accustomed to such stories. In fact many people will read this and barely bat an eyelid, but what does that say about us? We all have the opportunity to help any number of these children.

Laura Walsh

Loreto Secondary School, Fermoy, County Cork, Age 16

THE FUTURE OF A CHILD BORN TODAY IN THE DEVELOPING WORLD

... As many as one billion people – one out of every five people on our planet – are under-nourished and go to bed hungry each night. Not monthly, not weekly, but every single day, 19,000 people die of hunger and hunger-related diseases in the developing world. That is 13 people every minute of every hour of every day! Yet, humanity already possesses the resources, technology and the know-how to end the persistence of hunger and to prevent the death of little children, just like Azrielle. What we lack is the public will; the commitment to get involved.

The U.S. Presidential Commission on World Hunger stated, 'Whether one speaks of human rights or basic human needs, the right to food is the most basic of all. Unless that right is first fulfilled, the protection of other human rights becomes a mockery.' However $800 million a day, $33 million an hour, $555,000 a minute goes to the US Military Budget. The cost of one minute of military spending would provide food for 14,000 people for a month! I believe that the priorities of people with power in the world are completely upside-down and distressingly immoral. As declared by UNICEF, 'Another child will die in the time it takes to read this sentence. And the death of that child, a child who had a name and a personality, a family and a future, is a rebuke to all humanity. It is no longer necessary. It is therefore no longer acceptable.'

Unless Azrielle becomes the heir of a large inheritance, (which is extremely unlikely) she will join the 96% of girls in Malawi, who do not have a secondary education. (Hopefully, she will not end up in her mother's position of being in the 20% of females in Malawi who cannot read or write.) Azrielle's sister, Misozi, is lucky enough to go to a primary school. She must walk for an hour and a half each way just to get there. This makes a stark contrast to an affluent eight-year-old in the developed world who is transported to school with ease. However, Misozi considers this a small price to pay as many children in the developing world are desperate to go to school and learn how to read and write. For the majority of children, however, this is only a fantasy which will never become a reality, as no money denotes no education.

Sarah Finnegan

St. Dominic's Secondary School, Ballyfermot, Dublin, Age 17

THE FUTURE OF A CHILD BORN TODAY IN THE DEVELOPING WORLD

... A few days into my visit, I invited Dabir on a walk through the village. He hadn't been looking the best and I thought that maybe a walk would do him some good. Unlike some of the other villagers, I had become relatively close to Dabir and his mother, with his mother being the jolly, friendly woman that she is and Dabir just so young and lovable, I would have found it hard not to. After approximately five minutes of walking, I could see how weak and tired Dabir was getting. We began to head back to Dabir's mother. Halfway there I picked up Damir's frail body as he signalled to me that he couldn't walk any further.

When we arrived back at Demir's hut, his mother thanked me, gave Demir a quarter cup of water and sent him to bed, just as the sun was setting. That night, lying in bed, all I could think about was how dainty Demir's body felt as I carried him through the village, and his eyes. Those big brown eyes as they refused to stay open. I didn't sleep that night.

The following morning, I visited Demir to see how he was doing. Not great. He could barely lift his head off of the ground where his bed should be. He still managed to smile his traditional greeting when I entered the hut but his mother didn't. She knew. She knew what I knew. Demir was sick, Demir was very sick. He was also hungry and dehydrated. But the worst thing was, there was nothing we could do. I could tell that his mother wanted to feed him all the food and water in the village, and perhaps she would have, but Demir's deteriorating body refused to hold anything down. Giving him food or water would just result in him dehydrating faster. It was all too late ...

Eimear Deery

Largy College, Clones, County Monaghan, Ireland, Age 16

THE FUTURE OF A CHILD BORN TODAY IN THE DEVELOPING WORLD

There is another road that a child could go down in India. This one runs straight to a red-light district. Lots of girls become involved in the horrific world of prostitution. Thousands are sold in Mumbai ever year; then taken to Delhi, where they are taught to dress provocatively and how to apply make-up. In one bone-chilling story, a brother sold his two sisters in order to pay his debts. The youngest was nine. Another girl, aged eleven, was raped by four men, who were all over thirty-five. One man offered to marry her, in order to cover-up, or, 'resolve' the problem.

Once a girl is diagnosed with a disease, she will be cast out. If they have managed to save some money, they usually rent a hut. If they can't afford one, they die on the roadside. AIDS is the most common disease a prostitute will contract, and the women who get it are generally between the ages of fifteen and twenty. One teenager in an interview with MeriNews stated: 'We tell our customers to wear a condom, but they refuse.' The women, cannot pressure a client into wearing a condom, even if the man obviously has a STD. Girls who escape from this life, say that they feel 'alive'. They have gotten their freedom back. And in doing so, restore their dignity.

... Although the life of a child growing up in India may look bleak and hopeless to us, many people in India are able to find jobs that will keep them going and keep them happy. Although there are a few bad roads, children would not be lured into them so easily if the Indian government could improve the agricultural and rural sectors. Health, education and employment facilities are lacking, and if the government could focus its attention on these main factors, India would be holding true, to its high GDP and the future of Indian children, could be brighter, clearer paths.

Sarah Moan

Our Lady's Grammar School, Newry, Northern Ireland, Age 18

LESSONS WE CAN LEARN FROM THE DEVELOPING WORLD

Thankfulness ... It is the extreme poverty and struggle endured by these people that makes us aware of our own fortunate lifestyles and reminds us to cherish the privileges we enjoy such as a clean warm bed, the ability to attend school and the ease of mind we experience as we do not have to worry about where our next meal comes from.

Selflessness ... In many developing countries the selfish actions of corrupt governments has effectively oppressed the poorest of the poor. Power-hungry dictators abuse their positions and fail to recognise and appreciate how they acquired their positions – through the power of their people. Furthermore their inability to sympathise with their fellow countrymen is immoral and unjust. The situation in these corrupt countries allows us to truly value our human rights and all the things we are entitled to due to the nature of our democratic governments. We do not fear persecution or abuse for voicing our views and the luxury we have of being able to speak our minds is often undervalued until it is taken away.

Humility ... In many of the world's developing countries, illness is rife and often life-taking. In Africa alone, 22.4 million people are affected by HIV/AIDS, a devastating and incurable disease that orphans some 15 million children per year globally. This illness and others like cholera, typhoid and malaria prevent people who are already so incredibly deprived to work or provide food and shelter for their starving families, placing a huge burden on young children to leave school and work in factories.

Thanks to our current healthcare system and the abundance of specialised trained medical personnel, such uncontrollable levels of disease, thankfully, do not affect us. What's more is that we are privileged enough to receive education regarding hygiene and health, allowing many of us to be unaffected by the heartbreak associated with a premature death. In many ways we are humbled by our good fortune.

Moderation ... The rapid industrial boom in developing countries often widens the gap between the rich and poor and potentially leads to the exploitation and mistreatment of people for the sake of industrialisation and profit. In India for example the massive increase in city growth and urban sprawl has led to many people finding work in the so called 'informal sector' such as prostitution, child trafficking, shoe-shining and begging. Unfortunately this situation has arisen due to the government's unwillingness to encourage education and endorse school attendance as a means of breaking the poverty cycle. In addition multinational companies such as Nike are often offered cash incentives by said governments to come to their countries to boost the economy. Unfortunately this does not lead to a sustainable way of development and instead the government's seemingly good investment is wasted.

In many ways such economic booms can lead to overspending and excess, where materialism is placed above compassions to your fellow man.

Hayley Munroe

Ballinrobe Community School, County Mayo, Ireland, Age 16

THE FUTURE OF A CHILD BORN TODAY IN THE DEVELOPING WORLD

Where you are born will determine how you live. To whom you are born, also will determine the quality of your life, the kind of education you will receive, your health and wellbeing and medical care during the formative years, the kind of place you will call home, the food you will eat and the bed you will sleep in. The parents you were born to and the area of the world where you are born determines your opportunities in life, determines your potential and success, and if you are born in a developing country this is how life would be.

A child that is born today in any developing country does not have much of a chance in life. From day to day survival which ranges access to clean water and food to education, it is all about money. The future for such a child means being locked into the cycle of poverty and rarely is there a way out for such a child.

A child born today in the developing country faces a hard life, and if the child is female it faces an even harder life. The child has a high possibility of loosing their mother during the delivery, due to lack of energy, nutrition, aids also the simple fact that the mother delivered the child in a hut not a proper hospital, and didn't receive the proper medical assistance that she needed, and deserved. As a result of the death of the mother, this child will either be sent to an orphanage or else brought up by another family member.

... Life is a daily struggle for the children of Africa. The things we take for granted are simply absent in developing countries, from nutrition to hygiène, from education to the lack of books for reading. This is a life we have not experienced and it is not fair for a child born today to live this sort of life – they are only starting their life, don't they deserve a better start than this?

Sarah McNabb

St. Joseph of Cluny Secondary School, Killiney, County Dublin, Ireland, Age 16

LESSONS WE CAN LEARN FROM THE DEVELOPING WORLD

... On the 12th of January 2010, while Emmanuel and Martina were in school, the earthquake struck. No one in the school was hurt but it was a different story in their village. They arrived back to find their village was a huge mound of rubble, metal and earth. Some lucky survivors were pulled from the wreckage but Emmanuel's parents were not one of these.

Fourteen-year-old Emmanuel was left orphaned, distraught, scared and the new guardian to his little sister, all in the space of a day. He battled through four tough months, homeless, hungry and frightened, barely surviving every day. Things improved when Concern came to their village and helped them turn their lives around. He now has a home and some food, but as the sole earner in his family, Emmanuel was forced to leave school and work at a nearby farm.

He gets up at 5.00 am every morning, takes a forty minute bus journey to the farm and works nine hours straight in the blaring heat, with no breaks, all for $2.20 a day. He says that when he is tired, he thinks of Martina at home, hungry, and knows that he has to work or she won't be fed. Emanuel is very intelligent and optimistic and he hopes that when Martina is older and more independent, that he will be able to go back to school and train to become a doctor. So, the next time you complain about that stew for dinner, put yourself in Emmanuel's shoes for five minutes...

Maria Vanessa Rivera

Winter Park, Florida, Age 18

THE FUTURE OF A CHILD BORN TODAY IN THE DEVELOPING WORLD

Carlos Ignacio Torres Alvarez was raised in Comas, the most dangerous and poorest area of Peru. Ignacio's childhood was never easy. At the age of eight he began helping his father collecting plastic bottles. His sister Monica, the youngest, suffers from Wilsons Disease, a rare psychological disorder that builds up copper in the brain and the liver. This disease can only be controlled by a complicated and expensive treatment. The money Ignacio and his father earned barely sufficed for their family's basic needs. His parents could not finance the primary education their children deserved, so they had no other choice but to send them to a public school.

In developing countries the government often does not have the necessary resources to create a decent learning environment for students. Thirty students is the average class size in a public school, compared to a private school's higher attendance. Public institutions barely have finances to support so few students. Ignacio had to share a small, broken desk and bench with five other children. Yet, as he said, 'the school's condition was never a problem for me. At least I received an education.'

Like most of his friends, Ignacio spent his mornings and afternoons studying. Throughout the night, he would collect hundreds of plastic bottles in the street to bring some food home. Every morning he was exhausted because of the overnight work, but this was the expected price of an education...

Today, Ignacio is the Vice-President of Fluor S.A., the biggest system engineering company in Madrid. He has been able to buy a house for his parents, send his siblings to the best private schools and finance his sister Monica's treatment. Recently Diego, one of his siblings, was accepted to PUCP, the college Ignacio dreamed of before going to Spain. Ignacio's story demonstrates to us that being born in a developing world cannot keep a person from succeeding. There may be schools in terrible conditions, uncomfortable buses to take and other obstacles to overcome. However, as Ignacio said, 'Even in a developing world, success can be found, if you dedicate your life to pursue the treasure of education.'

Michele McHugh

Athlone Community College, County Westmeath, Ireland, Age 17

LESSONS WE CAN LEARN FROM THE DEVELOPING WORLD

... In the last number of years, the phrase 'Fair Trade' has become better known. Richer countries were exposed to the truth behind many of the products they consumed in large amounts. For example, coffee was being bought at ridiculously low rates from poor farmers in South America, Africa and India. These farmers lived in horrific poverty with their land being their only means of survival. Their coffee was packaged in fancy packaging and sold for a huge profit, none of which they received. The only person to benefit was the middleman. The lesson we have learned about coffee is only one of the many we can become aware of.

The Fair Trade Foundation educates consumers about this unfairness. We all now have the choice to continue buying coffee which is unfairly produced or pay a few extra cents for coffee which is fairly traded, where the poor farmer makes a profit and their family and indeed community benefit. A huge difference can be made, at very little cost to us in the Western world. The Fair Trade Foundation has extended its food produce from fair-trade flowers to fair-trade biscuits and sweets and even ice-cream. It's at our fingers to make a huge impact. They are now focusing on clothing and footwear too which are produced in 'sweatshops' in Asia. We as consumers cannot use ignorance as an excuse. We must put our money where our mouths are and learn to make a difference for people who desperately need our help.

The ultimate lesson we can learn from developing world countries is to have hope. Hope is what will give millions of children, mothers, fathers and families the will to survive. Don't ever discard hope. We can all pray and hope that our world can indeed change and can transform into a fairer and brighter place for everyone. Remember: it will be OK in the end. If it's not OK, it's not the end.

Part Three

COLLEGE STUDENTS
(Full or Part-Time)

FIRST PLACE – COLLEGE

Paul Kelly
Trinity College, Dublin, Ireland

THE FUTURE OF A CHILD BORN TODAY IN THE DEVELOPING WORLD

Kabula, Central Uganda

When I awoke to the sound of screaming, I stumbled out of my tent into the clear, African night sky whilst men and women all around me scrambled across the small dirt paths towards the sound of the cries. I spun around to grab a torch and hurried after them breathlessly. I arrived at the source of the screams quickly; however help was already on hand in the form of the Traditional Birth Assistant (TBA), Kaikara, who had already begun the process of delivering Acanit's baby. What Kaikara was doing was illegal, I knew, but I also knew that for Acanit, it was the only choice she had. As a widow of the civil war she had little money and could neither afford, nor face, the 60 kilometre journey towards the nearest health centre. As a result, like millions of Ugandan women, she was forced to rely on the now illegal TBA. Although Uganda's ministry for health believes these TBA's benefits to rural communities do not outweigh the potential risk from the under-trained and underfunded women, for Acanit, Kaikara had been a lifeline. Last year, her 12 year old daughter, Bacia, had been abducted by Joseph Kony's rebel Lord's Resistance Army and her husband had been killed trying to stop them. Widowed and alone, she now barely survives on the fruit of her small garden and the kindness of her fellow villagers. Travelling to a health centre had never been an option. Luckily, her pregnancy and subsequent delivery had been an uncomplicated procedure- unlike many others within the African state, with Uganda claiming one of the highest infant mortality rates in the world. This child had been lucky and was luckier still, in that he was unlikely to face the same fate as his sister, who was by now either dead, forced into prostitution or a soldier taking part in similar abductions and murders. For Najja however, Uganda has since entered an era of peace, with Kony's army being essentially destroyed by Operation Lightning Thunder- a joint military operation undertaken by the Ugandan and Congolese governments. The civil war has lasted 23 years but is now, at last, ending and as Kony's hold on rural areas becomes less and less, so do the child abductions. However, unfortunately for Najja, worries of abduction are replaced by more persistent, if not greater, problems. By the age of five Najja will begin his first steps in formal education in the small rural school close by his mother's own humble home. This right has now reached over 90% of Uganda's children and remains one of the paramount successes of Museveni's government. However, he, and almost half of Ugandan children will not complete this level, due to huge classroom sizes and having to work to help support his family, making his chances of reaching secondary level slim at best. Education is a difficult issue in Uganda as it is home to one of the youngest populations in the world, making it a logistical nightmare. Added to this, 35% of the population are under the poverty line meaning the malnourished children often find concentration very difficult, despite their strong work ethics. The small school in the village is both understaffed and overpopulated and Najja is unlikely to receive the high standard of education afforded in other parts of the country. Under these circumstances, by the age of 12, he is very likely to dropout to try and help support their small family and will join Acanit in the throngs of unskilled workers in Uganda's agricultural sector. The agricultural sector in Uganda accounts for 82% of Uganda's exports, the primary product being, as in many African countries, coffee. Coffee plants take up to four years to bear fruit, and prices fluctuate constantly, meaning for growers it is impossible to plan farming. This means the Ugandan government is consistently uncertain about how much money it can gain from taxes to finance infrastructure projects on an annual basis. This makes economic plans and forecasts meaningless and results in the agricultural sector being inefficient compared to its western competitors. However, development issues notwithstanding, this also puts Najja's job at risk. Additionally, he will be competing with cheap European surpluses which, under the Common Agricultural Policy, plague world markets. Although Najja will benefit from the EU's 'Everything But Arms' policy which allows tariff and quota free exports to the EU's markets, it is impossible for him to compete with the EU's highly mechanized farms whose produce continues to be subsidized. These difficulties will be further compounded by the global increase in temperatures as if these increase by even 2ºC it could essentially wipe out coffee plantations all across Uganda and will result in a rapid increase in rural to urban migration, which Najja will soon become a part of. Optimistically, by the age of 18, he will be one of the millions of slum dwellers who live in the capital city of Kampala, joining those who fled LRA attacks. Here, he will face a severe lack of running water as well as many ghettoized districts where entire villages fled from Kony's guerrilla attacks. In response to this, he is likely to use one of the many natural springs in Kampala, however, 90% of these are severely contaminated and every time he takes a drink of water he will risk cholera or other water-borne diseases. Indeed, the situation has now gotten so bad that over 50% of Kampala's inhabitants are hospitalized every 3 months by malaria, a disease borne by mosquitoes who favour the filthy springs. By the age of just 49 these, and a combination of malnutrition, poor sanitation, and pollution, will mean the death of

Najja. Najja's future is grim, through no fault of his own. His future is not one of unlimited potential, but of potential constrained by the cruel economic and environmental factors which will restrict his development. As I look upon this small child I am reminded of the United Nation's Millennium Development Goals (MDGs) and I wonder how long it will be before their effects reach him. Were poverty to be eradicated by the time he reaches primary school age, as the first MDG aspires to, his story and countless others, could be very different. However the sad truth is that until European powers put an end to the Common Agricultural Policy and a real effort is made to tackle global warming and the roots behind non-completion rates of primary education, this life is a certainty.

SECOND PLACE – COLLEGE

Soumitra Subinaya

National Law University,
Orissa, India

THE FUTURE OF A CHILD BORN
TODAY IN THE DEVELOPING WORLD

March 1, 2011, India:

As my air-conditioned car halts at the red traffic lights, five impoverished children, come running towards the car holding pirated copies of Kiran Desai's *The Inheritance of Loss*. They press their faces against the cool window glass of my car and coax me to purchase a book. The traffic signal turns green and I resume driving, leaving them running behind with the books. I see children in the roadside tea-stalls, washing used utensils or serving cups of tea to the customers. They are paid minimal and many a times subjected to abuse by both their employers and customers. The cobbler boy is beaten up black and blue if the brush erroneously touches the socks. The knick-knacks-seller-girl will have to sleep hungry if she cannot sell more than five items. The waiter boy is shown the door for not serving the glass of water a minute earlier and the helper boy is kicked out for eating a sweet out of hunger in the sweetmeat shop. The temples, the churches, the mosques, all have children standing at the entrance and exit gates, begging for few paise. The Oscar winning movie *Slumdog Millionaire* highlights the life of an Indian slum-boy, Jamal, who loses his childhood to abject poverty, starts earning by begging on the roads, stealing shoes, conning people into believing that the Taj Mahal

151

was a five-star hotel and finally switching to a livelihood of a 'Chaiwalla' or tea-server at a local call centre from where he makes it to a television game show winning a million in it. Sadly, the reality of Danny Boyle's movie ends at the 'Chaiwalla'. The truth is, one finds slumdogs millions here, each with his or her story of a bleak past and a bleaker future. The *New York Times* (March 12, 2009) reports that 42.5 per cent of Indian children under five are underweight. It states that India accounts for more than a fourth of the world's hungry (230 million hungry people) as per the latest World Food Program report. Estimates cite figures of between 60 and 115 million working children in India – the highest number in the world (Human Rights Watch, 1996). Pradeep Narayanan, Manager, Research at Child Rights and You (CRY), an organization working for children welfare, has official figures showing that less than half of India's children between the age 6 and 14 go to school. The CRY site states official figures indicating that only 38% of India's children below the age of 2 years are immunized and almost one in every five children in India below the age of 14 suffers from diarrhoea, an easily preventable disease. The latest World Bank estimates reveal that about 455 million Indians now live below the global poverty line of $1.25 per day (PPP). Thus, children in the developing world abound more in slums, are poor and without access to services required for human development. The infant mortality rates being high, many will not survive beyond three months. When I imagine the life a child born today in the developing world, I think of this 'common child'. The common child in the developing world is poverty's child. Being born into the poorest state of India, I personally have come across instances of mothers selling their babies for food and children dying of consuming mango kernels in the face of starvation. Behind the India-shining campaign is a disturbing reality. When I interviewed few families, seeking their perspectives on the future of a 'common child' born to poor families that outnumber families with adequate means of sustenance in India today, the answers were saddening. An interviewee replied, 'Such children will become rag-pickers, manual scavengers or beggars. They will inherit poverty and diseases.' Another replied, 'The common child in the developing world today becomes a commodity, which can be immorally trafficked and enslaved anywhere. If male, he becomes a criminal and if female, she is forced into prostitution.' None of the replies given by the ten interviewee families painted a decent future for the common child. These answers stated that the common child receives no benefit from the trickle-down-effect of industrialization and economic development being experienced by the developing world. The common child is getting increasingly marginalized and her/his future bleaker. In essence, the common child experiences, an 'inheritance of loss and privation'. The attention given to the common child seems minimal by the 'welfare' state and its modern people. An Indian newspaper editorial stated how 400 plus journalists were busy covering the Lakme India Fashion week on the front pages of their newspapers, while poor farmers (the community representing 70% of the Indian population) were committing suicides and their children dying of starvation. The developing world is experiencing an imbalanced economic growth which fails to be inclusive, sustainable, humanitarian and child-friendly. Such a development is jeopardising the common-child's future. Non-state actors such as NGOs and CBOs working in the field of livelihood creation, maternity and child care, and so on are the sole prominent hope-offerers for the common child in the developing world. Thus, an impartial scanning of the reality of the developing world today which includes the country from where I report and have been residing, provides one with a not so well picture of the common-child's future. However, to brighten this child's future the state and the non-state actors have to mutually and symbiotically cooperating and coordinating with one another create models for inclusive and sustainable development keeping the common-child's concerns and future in mind. Such inclusive and sustainable models of growth will enable the common child to enjoy her/his human and constitutional right to life, which as Justice Bhagawati of the Supreme Court of India in *Francis Coralie v. Delhi* stated includes 'a life with human dignity and all that goes along with it such as adequate nutrition, clothing, shelter and facilities for reading, writing and expressing oneself in diverse forms, freely moving about and mixing and commingling with fellow human beings'.

THIRD PLACE – COLLEGE

Shreya Maheshwari

Lucknow, India

LIVING ON LESS THAN $2 A DAY
IN THE DEVELOPING WORLD

If you are reading this, chances are that you have an elementary education, earn enough to eat two square meals a day, drink clean water and have access to basic health care in case of any emergency. The same, unfortunately, is not true for more than two billion people in the world who live on under two dollars a day – the official line of poverty as defined by the United Nations.

Hunger is a constant facet of everyday life for people here. Most eat whatever they can grow through subsistence farming. But as many developing countries are endowed with arid, uncultivable land, the produce is scant and devoid of nutritional minerals and vitamins required for healthy growth. The poor in urban slums are no better: they have to contend with high global food prices, and growing food inflation in most poor African and Asian countries means that two dollars a day puts very little food on the plate.

Two dollars a day also barely guarantees a roof over one's head, and walls around one's body can well be a luxury. Many families here do not own homes. Instead they live out in the open, in fields or urban footpaths or under temporary, thatched huts, in slums or villages, exposed to harsh climatic conditions. They are often surrounded by pools of stagnant water and waste, owing to lack of proper sanitation and sewage drainage facilities. Many drink this same water because clean water is expensive. As a result, millions are afflicted with life-threatening diseases like malaria and cholera, and even HIV/AIDS. However health facilities are meagre and most people do not have access to qualified medical practitioners or proper medicines to treat chronic, life-threatening illnesses.

Hunger and illness are acutely etched on the faces of many children here. Children from 'below poverty line' families are usually born in unhygienic conditions without basic medical care. Thousands of infants die young in these countries every day and those that do survive, grow into malnourished children, facing threats from infectious water-borne diseases, stagnant waste and dirt. Some are painfully thin with no muscle mass, their ribs etched out clearly against their blistered skins, sores and the dark shadows of depravation on their faces. Due to lack of nutrition and calories in their food, many of these children are stunted, as their physical development stops without adequate micro-nutrients.

Their families, struggling to make a living, cannot afford to pay for school fees and educate these children, perpetuating the cycle of poverty. Education is the passport to a better life but for many children in developing countries school is not an option. As a result of low human resource development, generations of a family are trapped in low income trades or low-productivity farming. Children are the future of our families, our nations and the human race, but most of these children are wasting away, not even living as human beings, let alone children.

Besides children, women in developing countries too suffer great hardships and challenges, as males are the primary wage earners here. Most women are dependent on the males in their families, and are exploited, at home and outside, but many go on suffering in silence and fear, bound by social norms and lack of economic freedom.

People who earn two dollars a day cannot make a living on such a wage; they merely survive. There are no social safety nets for them to fall back on and many of them are employed in conditions of great degradation, with little job and income security. It is impossible to overstate the psychological devastation, humiliation and insecurity that such poverty enjoins on people. Millions around the world live without human rights and basic necessities of life, often in conflict zones and under oppressive regimes. Poverty then becomes, many believe, as much a state of mind as it is a physical condition.

Despite these seemingly impossible living conditions, people still survive here. But is that enough? Modern hallmarks of the developed world --high speed internet, space explorations and fad diets to lose weight, seem absurd compared to the wasted potential and abject misery of almost half of the world which lives for two dollars a day. Even the two dollars they earn every day doesn't come easily to them. It is a result of great hard work and dedication, whether they are in fields or in factories doing manual labour. People here have great resilience and immense potential. It is evident in their constant endeavour to earn a decent living and strive for a better future. Successful programs of aid agencies like Concern Worldwide and microfinance organizations like the Grameen Bank, where poor people are given access to capital, skill-development and opportunities for self-employment, are evidence enough that given the right resources and opportunities to build a better life, most of the people in developing countries are empowered and can overcome all constraints of poverty to break its vicious cycle. Living with so little is not easy, but the constant struggle and effort of people here is a testament to their determination to make their lives amount to greater than the sum of its parts.

SHORTLIST – COLLEGE

Dorothy Mhlanga
University of Cape Town, South Africa

THE FUTURE OF A CHILD BORN TODAY IN THE DEVELOPING WORLD

Editorial: The Future for Africa's Children

Imagine being born in a place where going hungry every night is a daily part of life. A place where going to school is a luxury for the privileged few, where access to a doctor or medical care is rare, a place where parents die one after the other in rapid succession. It is difficult to imagine a harder or more challenging way to enter the world. This is the stepping stone upon which most African children move from in their journey through life.

Africa is one of the world's poorest continents with over 47% of people living in Southern Africa experiencing extreme poverty. Africa is also the continent with the most number of Aids victims and in turn Aids orphans. Over 22.5 million people are affected by the Aids virus in Sub-Saharan Africa alone. These facts coupled with a myriad of other problems combine to make a vicious circle of poverty and misery that many African children are born into and have little hope of ever escaping. This cycle serves to make the African child always dependant on hand outs and charity from the world. This is not because they are unable to work or that they are unwilling to actively contribute to improving their circumstances. It is because they lack the knowledge and the opportunities to acquire a means to change their situations for the better. Most children born in Africa today do not have access to the most basic of human amenities like clean water, enough food, medical care and an education. It is not difficult to imagine what the future holds for a child born in Africa under these conditions.

Having been stationed in Africa and after interacting with these children one realises that their hopes and dreams are to have the fundamentals that many people in the developed world take for granted. What they strive for are the basics of all human rights – the ability to hope for a better and brighter tomorrow. Children in Africa dream of going to school, yet because of financial problems or lack of infrastructure, the majority of them do not complete primary education. They dream of having reliable water sources and access to health care for their sick family members. Their dreams and hopes are ones that can be achieved through a combined effort. Africa has the highest prevalence of HIV and AIDS yet it is also the place that struggles the most to acquire anti-retrovirals. The time has come to help the African child move from being a victim destined to suffering and always reliant on charity to a self-sufficient adult in charge of their own destiny.

I imagine a brighter future for the African child, a future where being born in Africa does not automatically label a person as 'disadvantaged.' I imagine a future in which all African children have access to at least the most basic of medical care and treatment. I imagine a future where these children are able to go to school wherever they maybe be. I imagine them learning things that are relevant to their situation. For example if they live near the Sahel region where drought is prevalent and a major contributor to economic poverty, I imagine them learning more about better managing their limited water resources and ways of creating opportunities in their location. I imagine them learning the skills necessary to create a better future. At the end I envision the child born in Africa now an emancipated adult working toward building Africa.

These possibilities do not have to remain a dream. There are many international organisations working tirelessly to improve the situation of Africa's children and to secure their future. One such organisation is UNICEF. Through their education programs UNICEF has provided many children with an education and with this education they have given them the key to a better future. An education is a powerful tool for any individual. With knowledge one is able to make better decisions and to be more aware of the opportunities. African children need this the most. The past global economic crisis saw with it a decline in world spending power. The hardest hit during this time were the children in Africa who because of their reliance on aid suffered the most when donations were cut or lowered.

Plenty of work is being is being done to secure the future of Africa's children but unfortunately it is still not adequate. For every child in Africa that is educated there is another child somewhere who is not. More work has to be done to assist these children. Most importantly they need access to resources that will help them to empower themselves. In this way it is possible to mould the future of Africa's children into one with a positive outlook rather than what it is at present. With the World Bank predicting that over 47% of people in Sub-Saharan Africa will be living on less than a dollar by 2015, it has never been as important as it is now to help the African child. If nothing is done today we can rest assured that by 2015 we will have a global disaster on our hands. Today's world is so intricately linked and mutually dependent that a crisis of this magnitude in Africa will not only impact Africa but it will have ramifications across the whole world. It is crucial to act now and provide a future for the African child.

One of the most popular sayings from Africa is that 'it takes a village to raise a child.' It is this vein that I challenge the world and global leaders to not only imagine but to work collectively to create a brighter future for the African child. Let us as the global village raise the African child to be someone we can be proud of and most importantly let us raise an individual who is self-reliant and able to contribute to the improvement of the world.

SHORTLIST – COLLEGE

Sarah Maguire

University College Dublin, Ireland

LESSONS WE CAN LEARN FROM THE DEVELOPING WORLD

So often, we discuss the 'developing' world in terms of what they can learn from wealthier, more industrialised, more technologically advanced places, or the 'developed' world, as we call it. Perhaps, in some ways, the developed world is actually at a disadvantage, moving further away from a natural state and the enjoyment of the simple things in life. The old adage 'less is more' would seem to be true of life in the developing world, the biggest lessons to be learned from them; To be happy with what you have, to utilise creativity and ingenuity, and to be present in the moment. Incidentally, all lessons stemming from their being poorer, less industrialised, and less technologically advanced.

With overspending, debt, greed, and recession currently engulfing the developed world, it would be ignorant to think that we are the people who should universally dictate how society should be and how everyone should live. There are a lot of economic principles, among many others, that we can learn from the developing world. The first general lesson: be happy with what you have. It seems that, more and more, we are being indoctrinated into competitive, image-obsessed lifestyles of 'keeping up with the Jones's', always needing the latest thing, and spending well beyond our means to achieve this. We would do well to take a look at the developing world, at how they can only spend what they have, and at how they are resourceful and careful with what they do manage to afford. They waste nothing, while we let our

161

water flow down the drain, send copious amounts of food and objects to landfills, leave televisions on all day, spend money we don't even have, and work against rather than with our natural environment.

We've lost sight of the value of money, and also of the value of what we buy with money. We incorrectly prioritise fashion over function all too often, and indulge in the purchasing of luxury goods or gadgets that we probably don't really need. If we consider that some people in the developing world are forced to live on $1 or $2 a day, and if we consider that we would probably spend the same on chocolate, without hesitation, then we can see just how different our priorities are. While not begrudging anyone indulging in enjoyable activities, a critique on money being the main priority is in order. If people in the developing world can find pleasure and entertainment from non-material pursuits, surely we can do the same. In fact, we also used to be far more likely to do this in the past. Anyone who grew up before the 'technological takeover' of the developed world will remember how much more often they were required to use their imagination, and with limited funds and supplies, improvise and invent.

Fun is free. Say it with me (and the developing world.) Why do we think we need to spend money to be enjoying ourselves? When you have nothing, suddenly everything is something. A tin can is a mug, a bucket, a piggybank, a musical instrument, maybe even a walkie-talkie. Even back when I was a child, in the 90s, I made a musical instrument out of a tissue box, some rice, and some string, as a school project we all had to do. I proudly decorated it and was fascinated by the fact that it actually did make some kind of music, albeit nothing that is likely to be heard in the charts. Nonetheless, when I look back, I see a lesson in that project, a lesson that can also be seen when you look at the resourcefulness and creativity in the developing world. They may not have expensive drum kits or amplifiers but they can make and influence some of the most lively beats in music and dance. When we have less 'stuff', we use more of the human brain to do the work for us, and what a glorious instrument *that* is.

While people in the developed world must often consciously take the time to practice being present in the moment, by partaking in meditation, yoga, vacations, even therapy, the people of the developing world are constantly in tune with the present moment and with relationships, community, and nature. There is little laziness, procrastination, or convenience. Yet there seems to be more quality time. Everyone pulls together, everyone has responsibilities and roles for the common good, and in most cases, all interactions are face to face. People in the developed world are so focused on finding the quality time, so why don't they ever find it? It's not something to even be found, as if it's a mysterious entity playing hide-and-seek. It's right in front of you, and yours to grab or let drift away. Do a project with your children, pass on stories about the history of their ancestors, get involved with nature and our surroundings. Their informal education is just as important as their formal one.

We are not merely masters of the Earth, it is also our master. We have an interdependent relationship with it. We need to adapt ourselves to suit it, as much as we wish to adapt it to suit ourselves. In the developed world, we keep moving further away from nature and from the fundamental characteristics of life. Everyone has a different definition of what life is about and about the meaning of their lives, but we share one thing in common. We all live on the same planet, in the same world. We create the boundaries, the countries, the languages, the different ways of life, but we are all humans and in order to move forward, we need to share ideas, and share resources. There is something to be learned from every experience, and there only exists subjectivity, no matter how much we say we can be objective. Try to find the lesson, always try to find the lesson.

SHORTLIST – COLLEGE

Rebecca Keating
Trinity College, Dublin

LESSONS WE CAN LEARN FROM THE DEVELOPING WORLD

In our presumed sophistication as citizens of the 'developed world', we often consider ourselves a gift to the rest of the planet. We believed that our time of learning had been left behind. That we knew all that there was to know. In recent times the basis of this conception has fallen apart and we must begin to learn from others. More than ever, we began to be defined by how much we earned. The idea I earn, therefore I am. The car you drove, the house you owned, the clothes you wore all began to define us more than who we really were or what we stood for as a community. We became a society of material possessions and threw community to the wayside. This is a time when we have much to learn. Much to learn from the developing world who, although are developing economically, are developed in much more worthy ways.

Fear: It is a fear that people might think that you have less than others. So much of what drives people relates to their desire to maintain a certain appearance – a facade. We seek to present a false reality to all others around us. Not only is that an unhealthy financial habit, it is also certain to lead to a life of misery. We have begun to live our lives around something fictional, something unattainable and it is time to go back to basics. This fear has driven to miss out on human contact, affection, respect and community. To chase aspirations that don't truly matter to ourselves or those we love. To build a society that what built on excess not need: Greed not charity, material not morals.

164

Time for Change – That Time is Now: A financial crisis is shaking the basis of this rocky foundation. The incidence and ramifications of the crisis were obscure. Even now, the full dimensions and consequences are not known. Because the crisis is not yet over, among other reasons, we lack the perspective to develop a full appreciation of the lessons from the crisis, lessons that we must learn. What is real and what is financial? Yet looking beyond widespread anxiety about our economic prospects, we should perhaps take this opportunity to look at the bigger picture. We should embrace this time for change and to learn from the developing world about what is the true value of life. The idea that the ways that got us here, can keep us here is a falsehood. A falsehood we must reverse.

Lessons to be Learnt: John Wesley once said, 'When I have money, I get rid of it quickly, lest it find a way into my heart.' This is something which our society has failed to hear. Therefore, we must look to those who have not embraced the mantra of material importance. The developing world still holds the very ideals we once emulated; that living is not a by-product of earning. Embracing every moment of life is something which the developing world has yet to teach us. When you are so close to suffering, you surely see the value of every moment. We in the developed world are blessed with so many things we take for granted. These things make every moment more valuable. Yet, we ignore what we have been given in pursuit of more at the expense of others. It is true when Franklin Delano Roosevelt said, 'It is an unfortunate human failing that a full pocketbook often groans more loudly than an empty stomach.' We in the 'developed world' saw ourselves as individuals not members of part of a local and global community. We in the 'developed world' learnt to abandon ideals of community, in order to pursue goals that transpired to be mirages. Things that we fought so hard to achieve have been forgotten. Education is the most powerful tool of survival. In the developing world education is seen as being a road to freedom. Yet, we have begun to take even this most precious gift for granted. It is time to see what our neighbours in the developing world value and to see why we lost our way in the pursuit of entities that were as real as the credit we bought them with.

The Future: The real measure of your wealth is how much you'd be worth if you lost all your money. This is something we can learn from the developing world. A future we need to fight to build. Our time for learning is not complete. Our time for change is upon us. When I look at the developing world, I see a place of ideals, friendship, vitality, hope, community and life. This is the real purpose behind everything we seek to achieve. We lost sight of this goal. Now is a time where people must reassess their horizons to look to further borders for the vision we lost. To regain that sense of community. To become developed in the way that truly matters.

SHORTLIST – COLLEGE

Anastasia Gavrylova

Petro Mohyla Black Sea State University, Ukraine

LESSONS WE CAN LEARN FROM THE DEVELOPING WORLD

Eight Important Lessons We Can Learn

Once I was working on the Internet and quite by chance discovered my country in the 'List of Developing Countries'. It didn't change my attitude towards the country, of course – because I realize that the term 'developing' in the UN system is used for statistical convenience rather than for expressing judgment. But this made me think a lot about how it feels to live in a developing country – what we are strong at, what can be done better and what we can learn for future?

I was born when our country was facing serious political and economic changes. The whole nation was entering a brave new world without any clear vision for the future. My parents, both historians, characterize that period as follows: 'We were millionaires and we were the poor. Each new day could bring something unexpected. It was time of learning, mistakes and constant uncertainty. Indeed it was a very challenging time.' Under such conditions we formed a need for development, a longing for change. And the change followed – when I was two years old there came Independence with all its fears and hopes. Our nation, having a long diverse history, appeared finally as new country on a world map. And at once all usual paths and solutions vanished. It was the beginning and it was definitely not easy. But people were learning and country was changing. And it is still changing now. We as citizens definitely have a lot of work to accomplish: economy, environmental protection, political and education spheres – they all need to be changed in a way that they will respond to challenges of modern world. When somebody calls our country a developing one, it must me a signal for us: don't wait, start acting today!

'Do you have the patience to wait until the mud settles and the water is clear?'(Lao Tzu) – these words refer to the present time. We have now a clear vision of what we can learn from our previous experience. I want to name 8 main lessons... for all of us.

Lesson 1: Take responsibility. For this to happen something must change in the minds of people: there must be an understanding that responsibility starts with every citizen. If in a country people don't wait for someone to tell them what to do and don't blame others for misfortunes, but simply do what needs to be done – this is a perfect way to developed country! Our responsible actions create a better tomorrow.

Lesson 2: Make democracy a reality. Kofi Annan once said: 'No one is born a good citizen; no nation is born a democracy. Rather, both are processes that continue to evolve over a lifetime.' So we need to remember that democracy is not an idea, which exists on paper and can't be reached in real life, but democracy is a model to implement. We just need to start!

Lesson 3: Learn from history. Because 'history shows which mistakes we will make in future' (Laurence Peter), so looking back and analyzing past times helps to predict what can probably occur in future. Learning from history also means learning from challenges we have faced and from mistakes we have made.

Lesson 4: Share experience. Each country, developing as well as developed, has its unique path. There can be something very good and successful, and something that can be done better. Sharing own experience can be the best way of helping each other to become stronger!

Lesson 5: Value education. Education gives us freedom – freedom to think and to choose. Education doesn't give right answers but teaches how to search for them. Education broadens outreach and makes people care about what they have. What else does one need to help young leaders of tomorrow change own country from developing into developed?

Lesson 6: Believe in dreams. No progress and no change can be achieved without great passion and wonderful dream. Indeed 'the future belongs to those who believe in the beauty of their dreams' (Eleanor Roosevelt).

Lesson 7: Human Rights belong to us. And what is more important – they belong to us no matter where we live – in mountain region or by the sea, in big city or tiny village, in developed or developing country. And where there are Human Rights, there is a respect of every single person regardless of their origin, language or views.

Lesson 8: Don't be afraid of changes – be the change! This is perhaps the most valuable and inspiring idea one can learn from developing countries. Because we shouldn't forget, that countries are called developing, because their citizens are open to everything new – to changes, to new perspectives. And as soon as citizens realize they can themselves be the change – well we'll see how the world itself will change!

PASSAGES – COLLEGE

Mesfin Awoke Bekalu

Catholic University of Leuven, Belgium

THE FUTURE OF A CHILD BORN TODAY IN THE DEVELOPING WORLD

... Let me just mention two famous Amharic (the official language of Ethiopia) proverbs that the Ethiopian society possesses with regard to whether or not, and when to give birth, *'Lij be'lijinet new'* literally means, 'give birth to a child while you are too young', and *'Lij be'edilu yadegal'* literally means, 'a child will grow up on resources his/her luck affords him/her'. Such adages are deep-rooted and are likely to influence parents' overall thinking concerning whether or not and/or when to have a child. Chances are, therefore, high that a child will be brought to the world where s/he will not be aided to grow up in a way other children grow up elsewhere in the world. Parents who give birth to a child without prior plan concerning resources on which the child will grow up will just be sharing their meagre resources and are likely to make the next generation even poorer than they are. The fact that parents give birth without any plan and resources for rearing is best illustrated by another Amharic adage *'ene ebelaw sat'a lije tiris awet'a'* literally means, 'when I become poorer and have nothing to eat, my child grows teeth'.

... Overall, in this short article, my aim is to underscore the existing beliefs and practices of most parents as determinants of the future of a child born today in the developing world in general as illustrated among the Ethiopian society in particular. If we are to imagine a better future for a child born today in the developing world, mechanisms should be in place whereby societal beliefs and practices can be changed for the better. This being my main idea to share with, I am, also equally optimist that the overall development and poverty reduction efforts currently underway in most of such contexts would change the situation for the better and hence a better and prosperous future could be imagined for a child born today there. If the general public can be educated and the small positive beginnings observed here and there in the region can be scaled-up, the current practices of parents and the beliefs underlying them can be improved and a better and prosperous future can be imagined for a child born today in the developing world.

Kristopher Evans

The Australian National University, Canberra, Australia

LIVING ON $2 A DAY IN THE DEVELOPING WORLD

... Despite predictions that a more globalised world would start to bring an end to the struggles of those living on less than $2 a day, it can also be claimed that growing connectivity between nations is also exacerbating the issue. Increasingly powerful – and inexpensive – technology is still very much out of the reach of families like Josiah's, making it harder for them to engage with the world and, most significantly, for it to begin to understand either them or their situation. Instead of closing, the gap between the globe's highest and lowest rungs is arguably widening.

In most ways, the human tragedies we see and read about are just as removed from us as they were for our parents and grandparents years ago. The rise of global capitalism, with its associated penchants for gadgets and luxuries, has done little or nothing to stem the tide of poverty still engulfing the Third World. Despite the success and hard work of many dedicated anti-poverty campaigners over many years, the weight of the task grows and grows. Far from being an exclusive club in the 21st century, the Survive-on-$2-a-Day Club continues to expand its membership base.

Although the heartfelt appreciation of Eva and those around her for the charity they already receive is palpable, the food and other resources given are still grossly insufficient to break the cycle they face.

'People here do remember the help they've received,' Eva explains, in between keeping a fidgety Josiah from escaping through the open front door. 'My mother remembers the missionary women who helped deliver her children. But the pain, the misery, it still goes on regardless.'

Once again, Eva's words churn deep within me. For all our self-congratulations in the West on our philanthropy, we still often forget – or ignore, depending on your perspective – the enormous scale of the problems that remain in places such as this far-flung corner of southern Sudan.

Bernard O'Rourke

Dublin Institute of Technology, Aungier Street, Dublin, Ireland

THE FUTURE OF A CHILD BORN TODAY IN THE DEVELOPING WORLD

... The rest of Christopher's life will be unpredictable. Poor health conditions are not the only challenge he will face. Pakistan is the sixth most populated country in the world (after China, India, the USA, Indonesia and Brazil) and this population is growing rapidly. Overpopulation, and all the risks associated with that for a developing country, is a real concern for the future. Pakistan is also at massive risk form natural disasters. Earthquakes are frequent, as is flooding along the Indus River during times of heavy rain.

Christopher's life expectancy (if he can successfully escape childhood) is 64 to 66 years of age. The average time spent in education by a male child in Pakistan is eight years; Christopher is unlikely to receive anything more than a basic primary education.

In his life Christopher will probably migrate to one of Pakistan's growing urban areas, but this will by no means be a guarantee against poverty. While he has a good chance of getting at least some form of employment (unemployment is only at 15%), underemployment is a real danger. His working wage will not guarantee him an escape from poverty, with almost a quarter of the population of Pakistan (both rural and urban) below the poverty line. Like his parents he will have to survive on less than €2 a day.

Mark Kelleher

Open University, Milton Keynes, United Kingdom

LESSONS WE CAN LEARN FROM THE DEVELOPING WORLD

... Having lived in Somalia for 18 months, Siobhan has witnessed first-hand the cruel realities which separate Ireland from her new place of residence. 'You arrive here and you know all past complaints are all a bit silly, really,' she confesses. 'I suppose that's just the reality of the world, but still – you'd hope that a place like this would put issues back home into perspective.' Moments after our brief interview, Siobhan carries on distributing, and is met by a young man who carries his father to the distribution point in a wheelbarrow. They each get a bottle, smile, and wheel away once more.

My colleague and I, restrained by our impending deadlines, must leave again. He spends the last hour snapping shots of men hunched on dusty steps, whilst I sit and ponder what's around. From a clearing, Ayanna emerges once more, smiling again. She whispers a word I cannot decipher and palms me a cross woven from wood. I offer my thanks and hand her a sweet. Giggling, she sets off and I never see her again. I seek out her name, the meaning of it, and find it means 'beautiful flower'. We're taught to adapt to these things – to withstand the cruelty we must catalogue. We cannot change the world, as history has sadly proven -but we *can* try harder. However, we must first appreciate our downright luck, and learn from the misfortune we have somehow evaded.

Nishant Gupta

Netaji Subhas Institute of Technology, Delhi, India

THE FUTURE OF A CHILD BORN TODAY IN THE DEVELOPING WORLD

... It is now the year 2051: India today can boast the biggest and youngest population, which is an asset not only to the country itself, but to the whole world too. Of the country's total population, a significant percentage is in the working age group. Poverty in the developing countries is also taken care of. The young forces of politicians, in their 40s, of the developing nations, are resetting the demographic layout of the world.

What happened in India is, more or less, the story of many other developing nations. Where the fastest growing nations in 2020s-2040s were India, China, Brazil and Russia among few others, the 2050s would always be known as the time when African countries emerged from behind the shadows and that completely reordered the power distribution in the world.

China is a superpower, so is India. USA and UK, though still powerful countries, have shown a stagnated growth for almost a decade now. Africa is the emerging star, poised for a wonderful future like India was in the beginning of 21st century.

Change is the only constant in the universe. A new world order is in place. Developing countries are no longer developing countries ... and the reasons for this are those people, who dared to dream ...

174

Part Four

ADULTS

(Over 19 years old)

FIRST PLACE – ADULT

Mark Bennett

Forestville, New South Wales, Australia

LESSONS WE CAN LEARN FROM
THE DEVELOPING WORLD

This morning six women, bags balanced effortlessly atop their heads, walked out of the refugee camp into the deep haze of morning. They were singing as they set out to gather charcoal and wood for the day; a routine quickly established here in their new home. Like so many of the thousands of Ivorians who have fled their homes in the wake of the recent political unrest, they have found refuge in the Liberian town of Bahn.

Their songs were not sombre tones of lament, as one might expect given the huge personal loss and sorrow they have suffered, but songs full of joy and life. Children skipped along beside them, one boy in a bright yellow shirt laughing as he threw stones at a friend, missing by just a fraction and groaning to the sky in frustration like a footballer who had just missed that wide open net. His name is Emmanuel, and yesterday, at his school, insights were gained into the lives of these children and their future.

Emmanuel and his family fled Abidjan nearly two months ago. The violence spilling onto the streets has left hundreds of innocents dead. Like pawns in a game where the illusion of power means victory for a few but destruction for so many. Emmanuel's father was killed in their flight from the capital city of a nation that once represented the jewel in France's West African crown, La Côte d'Ivoire. Emmanuel and his three sisters, now fatherless, join so many of the conflict children in refugee camps throughout Africa.

Their mother Esther is one of the women I saw singing this morning, with tears in her eyes reflecting the soft morning light; tears not for what has happened, but for what can no longer be. 'I miss my husband,' she says in her broken English while watching the children play soccer with their brand new ball; one of the more popular gifts that had arrived that morning in a care package. 'He was a good man. Emmanuel is a good boy.'

His eyes are intense as he chases down the boy in front of him, no fear evident as he makes a sliding tackle on the hard dirt, much to the delight of the crowd gathered around to witness the event. 'The ball is a wonderful gift,' said Olivier, one of the teachers here at the school made of tents in which over two thousand students are educated; a number growing rapidly every day. This youthful looking man carries a composure that belies his age. His eyes are clear and focused as he talks openly about the opportunities they have to provide skills to these children for building a future.

A future that does not seem to exist on surface level examination, but Olivier is not deterred. 'They must learn,' he says passionately, 'so that they can have a chance in this world, to make something for themselves, to not be beggars or a burden.' Self-determination, a phrase heard often in Africa these days. His eyes intense, daring you to look away, he continues, 'We can give these them these things, we can teach them reading, writing, mathematics and computers. They have much to give the world. We have much to teach the world.'

His last point hits a chord as there is an unsettling truth in that single statement. It is they who have so much to give to us. The crowd bursts into cheers and Emmanuel embraces some of his team mates as they dance around holding the ball high in the air. This moment is theirs. The obstacles and challenges awaiting them as they grow into manhood seem far away, yet many of them carry the physical evidence of the real and current effects of those challenges.

Emmanuel runs over to his mother, face beaming with the pride reserved for the scorer of the winning goal. What would he say to the children in other countries who heard about his game today? He thought for a few moments, chewing his lip, before replying 'I would ask them if they like football? And maybe they can come and play with us one day. We have a new ball.' His big smile lights up his face, his eyes revealing a mischievous side. Then he is gone, running back into the big white tent for the afternoon's classes. Today they are going to have their first computer lesson.

Ten bright green laptops arrived yesterday from the OLPC, one of the many organisations working in the region. 'It's all about empowerment,' the Australian who delivers them says. 'To give these kids a future we need to equip them. This is just the beginning.' He keeps moving; no time to exchange names in the frantic days of the few who are building a vision for tomorrow. Not simply providing aid, but empowering; an idea that carries power and hope.

It is this hope that can be seen in the faces of these children, in the smile of the Emmanuels and the conviction of the Oliviers; a hope that presents an undeniable challenge for rest of the world: that in the faceless mass of the children of this vast continent, there is the face of humanity, and the hope for her future, a future that can be built upon an exchange of resources for the gift of a generation that carries such wealth within its children.

The women return to the camp, their songs still alive as the heat of the morning sun builds. Their loads are heavy with fuel necessary to sustain the cooking fires that will feed their children. Their sorrow is great but in the eyes of their children they see joy. And we can see the future of our world.

SECOND PLACE – ADULT

Ace Pelayo
Adult High School,
Ottawa, Canada

LIVING ON LESS THAN $2.00 A DAY

Reporting for *The Manila Bulletin*
Dateline: March 25th, 2011
Place: Payatas, Manila, Philippines

Drugs, crime, corruption, and war in the south are just some of the problems in the Philippines, but the major problem is poverty. You don't need to travel down south to see the crisis. Even the Capital itself has its own version. Over a million people in this crowded community near the dump site have no clean supply of water, no access to medication, and no help from the government. I am Ace Pelayo reporting for the *Manila Bulletin*. I'm in Payatas Village in Manila to see how people here manage to survive on less than $2.00 a day.

One of the people I meet is Phil, a middle-aged man living with his wife and seven children. Phil came to Manila from the provinces 30 years ago. He hoped to find a good job, but he ended up working at the dump site. His wife has no job and only three of their children go to school. The four oldest children dropped out to help their parents earn money.

The family lives near the dump site where Phil works. Every day, Phil wakes up at 4.00 in the morning. He cleans the tools he needs for work. These are the metal hook with a sharp end that can pierce anything and the plastic bin he uses to store the things his family collects. While Phil is getting ready, his wife cooks breakfast, usually eggs and 'tuyo' (dried fish). At exactly 6:00 am, dump trucks come to throw out the garbage they've collected from all over the city. Phil grabs his tools and goes out the door quickly. The horn from the dump trucks means it's time to work.

I expect that we will be the first to arrive at the dump site, but I am wrong. As early as 6.00 am there are already tons of people starting to collect garbage. I am shocked to see young kids, five to ten years old, gathering tin cans to sell. I ask one of them, 'Are you saving this money for something?' He answers, 'Yes, I am saving money to buy sandals so that when I step on something sharp, my feet won't get hurt'. I think about how at a very young age these kids are aware of their situation and they are helping themselves.

Phil told me that some kids here choose to collect garbage over going to school because they can't afford the tuition fees. They think that collecting garbage will give them instant money to help their parents. It's like choosing the nickel today over the dime to-morrow.

I notice that people don't have any protection from germs or bacteria caused by flies, cockroaches and rats. Phil says that they can't do anything about it. They need to earn money. He says,' I am doing this for almost 35 years now. I am used to it, but some-times you can't prevent illness. Luckily, a missionary comes to the dump site to give free medicine to us. That really helps us because almost all the kids here are prone to sickness.' I ask if the children know the consequences of jumping on a pile of garbage and risk-ing their health just to earn money, but Phil tells me they're fully aware of it, 'It's not that we want to get sick, of course we don't, no one wants to get sick, it's just that we need to in order to put food on our table.'

After a day of collecting garbage, Phil sells all of it for 89 pe-sos, or almost $2.00. He says that he is lucky today because he usually earns less. I ask him, '89 pesos? Is that enough?' Phil answers, 'it's better than nothing. I buy whatever I can with this money, but sometimes it's just not enough.' I ask how many times his family eats a day. 'We eat twice a day when there's enough garbage to sell.' How will he spend today's money? 'Maybe I'll buy some pork and a little bit of rice. You know, we only eat pork or beef once a month because we can't really afford it. Sometimes, I just want to give my children something special'.

THIRD PLACE – ADULT

Cristina Kessler
St. John, Virgin Islands, USA

LIVING ON LESS THAN $2 A DAY
IN THE DEVELOPING WORLD

Zooming across the Sahara Desert, I watched the endless desert sands of the Sudan roll away. Suddenly unexpected lines of women carrying heavy, swaying water containers on their heads would appear. They strutted in the heat and the dust of the open desert plains, many with a baby on their back. And all of them laughing or singing. It was humbling.

These women were the living example of 'Making the best of a difficult situation'. Even in the harshest of conditions, with no transportation choices or options, and endless hard work, they laughed or sang or joked their way through the day, living a true community-based existence.

Life as a rural African woman is beyond difficult. We spent 19 years in Africa, with Peace Corps and an NGO. We went to places not on roads or maps, where every day is a struggle, where the women keep the villages going, through their hard work and dedication to family.

Women living in the scattered villages we visited explained how they spent more money buying water in a year than buying food. How they grew sorghum and millet, producing enough to feed their families. One old woman, wizened by sun and age, told us, 'We grow groundnuts and sesame, as our cash crops.' If they get good rains the family may make $250 in a good harvest year. That's approximately $1.46 a day, for families of six or seven. Food, water, school fees and school uniforms all came from this money. And most of it is earned by the women.

Women are the backbone of Africa. Every day they collect firewood, haul water, hoe fields, beat laundry, pound grain, cook the meals, feed the children and men, and most importantly, make sure their children go to school; and all on less than $1.50 a day.

For years I thought programs should be focused on women, rather than men, for a more responsible response. The village of Jaffla proved just that on the day we visited. There was one large thorn tree growing in the square of the village of mud huts. A sea of beautiful women sat on prayer mats in the dust, ready to hold a meeting.

A project had recently begun, and the women were boisterously gathered to learn how they could receive what we would consider very small loans, to start their own income-generating projects. They were there because they were offered an opportunity to improve their families' lives, an opportunity that no African woman, no matter how busy she already was, would refuse.

It was a social event as well as a meeting. The women were a beautiful array of skin tones and cloth colours, features and jewellery. A few wore gold nose rings, while some others had gold bangles or necklaces. Each wore yards of stunning cloth wrapped around their bodies and draped over their heads. They were dressed in their finest, as if going to a wedding. The social gathering ended when the same old woman we had spoken with during the afternoon called it to order. She clapped her hands and soon all the women clapped, then suddenly it stopped with a resounding silence.

The women, dressed for a party, got right down to business. First item on their agenda was to select a Board of Directors for their new organization. They had the unusual distinction of having six literate women amongst them, so no men were needed for the board. A series of ululations filled the air. Next they elected a treasurer. The woman chosen told everyone that she could not read or write, so maybe she wasn't the best choice. But the women reassured her that she had been elected because they all had faith and confidence in her honesty. She humbly accepted the position.

The floor then opened to the members to discuss what businesses they would start. One group would be buying chickens, to sell eggs. Another group wanted to make candles. Some wanted to buy cloth to sell in the market, and a few hoped to buy a donkey and cart to charge for delivering water. The ideas flowed and the energy built as plans were made that would add hours to their already full work days. Hours that might take them into the $2.00 a day category. The group leader silenced the women again for another announcement.

Two NGO fieldworkers spoke of a seeds and tools program the women were already involved in. Seeds for millet and sorghum were provided, along with hoes. In exchange the women had to build storage units to house the seeds they got from their harvest, and repay the seed bank for their original loan. They would each have a bigger harvest and their own personal seed banks as a result. The ululations erupted when they learned that their women's group had already repaid 93% of their loan, while the village men in the same program had repaid only 33%. 'GO WOMEN!' I shouted out. The women cheered my encouragement.

I felt like I had received a huge gift – for their joy had become mine. As I thought about their labor-intensive days in one of the harshest environments in the world, I also thought about how these women turn the most difficult daily challenges into as much fun as possible. They worked together, and struggled together, and also celebrated together. Life's challenges were just life, and making each day as positive as possible involved working together, singing and joking.

Just about sunset I received another touching gift. Three women came into the compound, after walking two hours from Jaffla. They brought me a fried chicken and 11 hardboiled eggs, as a sign of solidarity, showing me that no matter how different our lives may be, we are still all connected. These women, amongst the poorest in the world, taught me lessons by their daily approach to life that I will never forget. Lessons we all can benefit from.

SHORTLIST – ADULT

Brian Harding
Tallaght, Dublin, Ireland

LESSONS WE CAN LEARN FROM THE DEVELOPING WORLD

Travels across Africa and Asia have revealed there is a lot to learn and be replicated at home. The Millennium Development Goal 7 focuses on our global agenda towards creating a more sustainable world. We often look to our Scandinavian neighbours to be the leading light in such environmental matters. Wind power, green cities, separating green and brown electricity generation, cycling promoted, excessive oil use castigated, waste recycling have advanced the reputation and fundamentally the healthiness of lives of the people that reside there.

We can learn from our neighbours all across Europe; however, it may be wise to begin to look toward activities that happen in the developing world as guidance in how to drive a new way in building a more environmental and healthy future.

As I travelled across Kenya I met Marta, a 27=year=old mother of two. 'I could be a very old woman before the government can provide my entire village with regular electricity. We are very far away from the capital city. But I want my children to be able to read and write and do their school work and I need light for that.' Further along the dirt track where Marta lives, her friend Anne Wanjiru described how she took a loan off a microfinance project and bought a foot pump lighting system. 'I pump for 20 minutes and we get up to 14 hours light. I don't have to buy kerosene anymore. I will have fully paid back the loan by the end of this year.' These empowered women are not waiting for the government to supply the energy needs of their family – they are taking it on themselves. They realize by harnessing alternative forms of energy they can address immediate issues that are challenging them and their families. They have seen the benefit of investing in their energy needs. Can we also see the benefit of putting larger upfront costs toward better insulating our homes and using small wind and solar systems to gain better economic returns in the long term?

In neighbouring Uganda, I realized the economic benefit that the country has garnered from protecting their gorilla populations. Mountain gorillas are some of the rarest in the world. Hunted ruthlessly in the past – they are now seen as an important part of the economy, generating $ 13.2 million in foreign exchange earnings and generating 1,000 jobs. It has become a cornerstone of the Ugandan tourism sector and national economy. But gorillas don't live in isolation. They are an important part of the forested mountains of Uganda. They are as much a part of the ecosystem as the trees, plants, insects and mammals that make up these wet environs. By protecting all of the forest and not just the gorillas, the government of Uganda has given its people the chance to be part of tourism as a whole but also maintain forests which offer medicinal plants, construction materials and seasonal foods when managed properly. Looking home, are we truly utilizing our natural resources to their full extent? Many of the natural wonders of our country go unnoticed – as salmon leap up great weirs on return to spawning grounds, as whales pass our coasts, as golden eagles traverse our countryside and as badgers and other interesting mammals scuttle around at night they offer the humans that live alongside and above them great opportunities.

Travelling to the high mountains of Nepal I have seen how the people there have taken steps to address climate change. For these people, climate change is not something to be debated - it is very real. In the district of Solukhumba, a large lake has been forming. Imja Lake did not exist in the 1960s, today it is one square kilometre in area. Imja glacier which communities here have been looking up toward for centuries has been receding by up to 75 metres a year. Where is the glacier going? Well mostly melting into Imja Lake. The people are worried. They should be. A newly formed lake that size is dangerous and visiting geologists have said the same. Local people have waved the flag and asked for help. They need the best of modern science and financial resources but they are happy to do the work. They have heard of projects in Bhutan where local people have begun to slowly drain the water from the lakes that have formed near their communities. It is hard tiring work and requires communities spending time at high altitude hammering away at rocks. No large construction equipment is here or can get here. The communities are isolated. They are adapting to climate change themselves. So, what's the lesson? Surely, we are beginning to wake up to the reality of a changing climate. It is the shocks that will hurt the most in many cases – the unexpected snows, the unusual or prolonged flooding events- which will threaten our lives and livelihoods. The peoples of the high Himalayan Mountains don't want to be on the receiving end of a flood that could turn into a tidal wave flowing down toward their villages, they are taking the battle to the problem and addressing on site.

It seems that governments in the developing world are waking up to such environmental shocks. They don't have as much money as governments in the developed world. One of the ways that they have begun to cut costs is to look at how poverty and environmental protection are linked and making savings in one can have an impact on the other. In many developed countries we run separate ministries and agencies that do not speak to each other. This is simply not viable anymore. The staff of the Ministry of Environment should have a good understanding of the work of all Ministries and vice versa. This should be true for many areas. We should be looking from top to bottom in our country for answers to our problems and most definitely toward our African and Asian neighbours for added guidance.

SHORTLIST – ADULT

Jody Harris
Newick, East Sussex, England

THE FUTURE OF A CHILD BORN TODAY IN THE DEVELOPING WORLD

A child born today is born into a world of just under seven billion people; if that child reaches her 18th birthday, she will share the planet with over eight billion others, and the world is likely to look very different.

A child born today will be four years old in 2015, the year the world measures its successes in development with the Millennium Development Goals. These goals include reducing the impact of hunger and disease, improving fairness between boys and girls, and reducing the huge number of preventable child deaths; every day, 26,000 children under the age of five die prematurely, so a child born in the developing world today has to fight to have a future at all. If she wins that fight, the first 1,000 days of life, from conception through to two years old, are crucial for her future health and productivity; the nutrition of her mother, whether and for how long she is breastfed, and whether her family have access clean water and to the quality and quantity of food she needs for healthy development in this period will affect her chances for the rest of her life.

Regardless of whether or not she has these basic necessities, a girl will be worse off than a boy born into the same set of circumstances. If the imbalance between boys and girls and men and women is not sufficiently addressed in her lifetime, a girl born today is twice as likely to remain illiterate, and is far less likely to have a say in the running of her life, either at home or in the political realm. Vast international efforts are already underway to improve her access to education, the most powerful tool she will have in addressing this gender imbalance and improving her own life and that of her children.

In most parts of the world, it is likely that a child born today will have fewer children than her mother did; fertility rates are falling as science and technology allow more children to survive and reduce the need for large families. Despite a declining population growth rate however, the population will still be growing, and she will likely live through panics over food shortages and more food price fluctuations if the underlying causes of food price volatility are not addressed. The planet will be able to feed her and her children, but only if farming practices improve in all regions of the world, and if access to the food that is produced is made more equitable. Rather, the major worry as she ages will be water, or lack of it; countries with the highest population growth will also be those with most pressure on water resources, and even in water-secure areas billions will not have access to adequate water for drinking and sanitation if current trends continue. Over her lifetime, the true impacts of climate change on extreme weather events will also become apparent, and their impacts on humanity clearer.

Though she may have been born in a rural area, a child born today will be more likely to live and work in a city; in 2008, for the first time in history, more than half of humanity lived in urban areas, and the process of urbanization is set to continue. Although the poverty surrounding her will be higher in an urban area, the opportunities for her to escape poverty will also be more abundant in the city, if she is equipped with the skills and knowledge to do so. She may have been born in one of the fast-growing economies of Africa, or among the 40% of humanity living in China and India; either way, she is likely to see a major shifting of power from Western governments to these emerging giants and subsequent economic and political changes in her lifetime.

A child born in the developing world today, if she overcomes the hurdles she faces through an accident of birth, and if she is able to take advantage of the improvements that are gradually happening in women's rights, education, and health, has every chance of living to an old age. Average world life expectancy is 67 years and increasing, and is the one area in which women generally do better than men. However alongside longer life, economic development brings demographic and nutrition transitions, and therefore the diseases of affluence; if she has done well in life, diabetes and heart disease may dog her in older age.

A child born today in the developing world has a better chance than she has ever had to rise out of poverty, to maintain her health and support her family, and to live a long and productive life. The challenge for the world she is born into is to increase the rate of these improvements while minimizing the risks to health and ecosystems of a more developed, globalized world. Ultimately, a child born today has the right to expect that we leave the world a better place for her and her children.

SHORTLIST – ADULT

Caroline Finn

Kinnegad, County Westmeath, Ireland

LIVING ON LESS THAN $2 A DAY IN THE DEVELOPING WORLD

Global Review. March edition 2011.

Our man H.J O'Fhinn in South Africa gives an insight into the life of the Swalhajalli family. Despite financial struggles that would have an Irish family clawing their hair out and migration on a national scale the family unit shows true courage and dignity which would put us to shame.

Driving along the dirt road into the Junja Township, twenty kilometres west of Johannesburg, the dawn sky, lilac sliced with slivers of rhubarb pink is breath taking, nestled deep in jagged navy mountains. Logging is the main industry on these mountains. Dozens of trucks raising rusty red dust clouds speed past me and the throngs of workers walking or bussing it into the city.

I arranged to meet a typical township family, and share their story with the readers of *Global Review*. Mrs Swalhajalli at the age of sixty eight is the full time carer of her three grandchildren. She tells me, their mother, Daisy works in Jo'burg.

We squat low before a plastic tray where nuts, bitter herbs and cups of a hot ruby liquid have been laid out. She gestures for me to eat. She takes up a pinch of purple herbs and grinds them with her remaining brown teeth, smiling with satisfaction as if she has just consumed a grand feast.

Tanya is ten. She attends the local primary school. When she is finished her homework and folded away her uniform she must climb the hills and gather sticks from the undergrowth of the teak plantations. This stack of boughs and twigs she secures in rope and lugs home on her back. Her grandmother will use them as kindling to start the fire to cook their meals.

Lilly, her oldest granddaughter, comes in she wears a faded oversized dress. She finds the family's one pair of communal flip flops. 'I'd never go into the city bare foot' Lilly tells me, appalled, when I rather foolishly asked who decides which of you gets to wear them.

Her Grandmother waved her off. She turned to me with that smile of hers, she says something in her local dialect, loosely translated it means 'Lilly is young and has her pride, she doesn't want people to think we've no arse in our trousers!'

She misses a day of school each week, to bus into Jo'burg in order to meet her mother. She doesn't go to the house where her mother works as a live-in housekeeper and nanny. Her employer Mrs Van der Smit doesn't allow staff any visitors. So she meets her at the market where she grocery shops for the Van der Smits. Daisy gives her a package containing bones left over from the meals they ate that week. On a good week Lilly could carry back lamb chop bones still with scraps of meat attached or a chicken carcass.

It is late when she gets home. Her grandmother adds herbs and boils up the bones. This broth will supplement their main meals during the week, usually cornmeal with a scattering of vegetables from their small garden patch. Her daughter-in-law sends some of her wages back each week. Lilly pins it safe into her pocket. This money works out at just under two dollars a day. Her Grandmother will buy necessities: meal, cooking oil and charcoal. She also needs to pay for schooling. There is no free education. The children's mother has tried to instil the importance of proper schooling to her children. Lilly wants to be a teacher. Her brother Gurup who is just eight wants to work on one of the large wildlife reserves. He knows he will have to move away from his grandmother, to Kenya. In order to do that he must get good exam results. Before Lilly goes to bed she runs to her school friend Magda for the lessons that she missed in school that day. She studies them herself at home.

Their father went away to work in South African mines five years ago. News came to the family that he had contracted aids. He spent months in hospital before he died. Daisy is still paying off his medical bills. The international gold mining company are pursuing her for monies they say her husband owes for food and accommodation. Mrs Swalhajalli told me the family never saw any of his wages, forcing Daisy to work in Jo'burg away from her young children.

The walls of the corrugated shack are pasted in glossy magazines, which Mrs Van der Smit had sent them, saying, 'Your girls might like to flick through them,' Mrs Swalhajalli recalls, a faraway look in her eyes. A single bare bulb hanging, precariously wired to a battery provides their only light. Washed school shirts are drying in the hot sun, despite no washing machine or running water, they are a dazzling meringue white. I thought of all the money wasted in Ireland on Vanish and fabric softener.

Mrs Swalhajalli rises before dawn. She milks their tethered piebald goat. Her hands are knuckled with arthritis and the whites of her eyes have a yellow tinge. A tear runs off her cheek as she says she worries about her frail health, in case she can't look after the children.

She mixes ground meal and goats milk, stirring it over a charcoal stove into a semolina consistency. This traditional breakfast, she tells me, fills up the children's stomachs until evening. I thought of the coco pops my children slurped up, while glued to morning cartoons. They were usually hungry again in an hour.

A letter had arrived that day from their mother; she would be home in a fortnight to celebrate Labour Day. The children's grandmother was excited and couldn't wait to tell them when they arrived in from school.

I left that day. The Swalhajalli's are no different to the thousands of families in the Junja Township scraping by on very meagre funds.

SHORTLIST – ADULT

Thomas McCarthy

Summerhill, Cork, Ireland

LESSONS WE CAN LEARN FROM THE DEVELOPING WORLD

'Crisp Sheets, Cholera and Creole': A report from a beleaguered Haiti

I currently sit in a dilapidated hotel room in Port-au-Prince. By local standards however, it is a palace, with clean linen and running water. Perhaps the most attractive feature is that it offers asylum from the stench of death and fear that stalk the Haitian streets. Footsteps crunch on the rubble-laden pavement outside my window, one of the many vestiges of the 7.0 earthquake that decimated the nation over a year ago. My decision to remain in the increasingly disease-ravaged capital raised my editor's eyebrows and hopes of a breaking story in equal amounts. I am in poor company – many of my colleagues have deserted for the richer pickings of Bahrain, Fukushima and Cheltenham.

Haiti, the poorest country in the Western Hemisphere, has an unfortunate history. From its initially promising inception (a successful slave rebellion is a rare event), it has been challenged by political upheaval, poor environmental policies, natural disasters and now cholera, a disease that had been absent for decades. Everything seemed different in the aftermath of January 2010 how-

196

ever. Despite the awful consequences, in a sense it offered a unique opportunity to rebuild a nation fractured long before the ground shook. Nature had leveraged a bulldozing that would never have been sanctioned by man, and with this came the promise of billions in tandem with the support to utilise it justly. The bulk of this aid has not materialised nearly eighteen months later. Of course this is nothing new – La Perle des Antilles has been allowed to wallow for decades, with little prospect of bettering itself. The fact that it holds no oil or mineral reserves is indicative of the West's hypocrisy. The only choice seems to be for Haitians to wake up and smell the coffee, their main export.

Perhaps the one stressor Haiti has so far been relatively spared is the spirit of rebellion sweeping the Middle East and North Africa. The exercising of a right we often take for granted is borne of extreme oppression, an action often met barbarically by the powers that be. Recent Haitian first round elections were plagued by rumours of tampering, which resulted in several days of rioting in December, and a re-count. Violence has overshadowed the electoral process, but not on the bloody scale seen elsewhere this year.

The mood on the streets now, however, is visibly upbeat. News has broken of the withdrawal of government-backed Jude Célestin, who an initial ballot had indicated as a strong contender. This now leaves the population with two seemingly independent choices, and yet some critics feel Haiti bowed to international meddling. Whatever the motivation, it is fortunate timing. While a citizen standing up for his rights represents perhaps the last bastion of dignity, it could bring to the fore deadly consequences. Cholera, a rapid killer characterised by watery diarrhoea and vomiting, is the biggest concern. The disease spreads with ease via contaminated food and water, and thus makes large gatherings a recipe for disaster. While the United Nation has estimated that over 400,000 Haitians will contract 'Kolera' this year, a new Harvard Medical School study actually estimates this figure to be closer to 800,000, including 11,000 deaths.

What then can we learn from the misery of the Haitian legacy? The concept of gratitude comes to mind – for the simple things like food security, or having the choice to demonstrate peacefully and not endure a baton charge. The fact that we never seem to bother protesting in large numbers should concern us all, however. It is a mode of passive resistance Egyptians and Tunisians have been desperately embracing and indeed dying by the score for. One could argue our apathy is a by-product of democracy, others proffer it is a deficit in the Irish psyche – this notion of raising hell among family and friends by moaning about an issue, but a failure to act when it comes down to brass tacks. Our muted reaction to a penal bailout comes to mind, or the inexplicable length of time a hopelessly inept government was allowed continue the charade.

A modicum of perspective would not go astray either. Yes, an Irish default may be on the cards, underscored by the loss of homes as banks foreclose on frankly obscene mortgages. Yet life goes on. Countries have defaulted before and emerged intact. We will have to endure a hit on our standard of living, and inevitably those who fuelled the crisis will not feel anywhere near the pain they should. However, lifestyles will still be vastly more comfortable than the absolute poverty 80% of Haitians experience daily. I marvelled at the international celebration of Irish culture on March 17th for St. Patrick's Day. Despite our troubles, we still have a future worth embracing. Haiti and countries of a similar ilk cannot entertain this outlook. They were handed a raw deal from day one, whether through coups, corruption or colonialism, and have struggled ever since to break free from the stranglehold.

Perhaps the final lesson on offer from current world events is best illustrated by a rapidly changing Libyan landscape. Weeks of indecision by both the West and Arab League have allowed tyrannical Colonel Gaddafi to maim and murder at will. The eventual imposition of a no-fly zone was met with a specious promise of ceasefire, necessitating the move all the more. Sometimes taking too long to make a decision can be more detrimental than the action itself. Not following through, such as delivering on the promise of an active role in rebuilding a broken community, can be the most damaging of all. Until the West decides to overhaul its ethical compass, Haiti's path will remain unchanged.

In the ironically named Cité Soleil (Sun City) – a slum regarded by the UN as one of the most dangerous places on earth – talk of gratitude, perspective and smart decision making ring hollow. Most of these people only know pain, and have little reason to think differently going forward. Will the upcoming elections, and the hitherto unrealised commitment of the West, change their minds?

SHORTLIST – ADULT

Lian Thang

Adult High School, Ottawa, Canada

LIVING ON LESS THAN $2 A DAY IN THE DEVELOPING WORLD

Reporting for *The New York Times*
Dateline: March 23rd 2011
Place: Myanmar, Chin State

I'm now in Lungpi village in Chin State, Myanmar. The weather is hot today and it is quiet except for barking dogs, crowing roosters and crying children. I meet a woman who lives in the village, and she tells me about her family's poverty-stricken life.

Ngun Tiak is only 42 years and the mother of three children. She looks old because of her hard life lived in increasing poverty. Five years ago, her husband died while carrying the Burmese army's rations and ammunition through the jungle. Now this poor widow and her three children live in a small thatch cottage, facing a very hard life.

The mother works in a government-run agricultural garden, earning 800 kyats (equivalent to $1.00) a day. Her total monthly income is 16,000.00 kyats or $20.00, which is enough to buy only one and a half tins of rice. She works 10 hours a day starting from 7:00 am to 5:00 pm and then works an extra two hours in her private corn field. She gets up at 4:00 am in the morning and takes two hours to cook the family's lunch. After finishing her breakfast at 6:30 am, she sets out for the agriculture garden and reaches the work place at 7:00 am. At 5:00 pm Ngun Tiak comes home for a few minutes rest, then continues working in her private garden until it is dark. This is how Ngun Tiak spends her daily life.

Ngun Tiak cannot afford her children's education. While their mother is working all day, her three children waste their time doing nothing. Ngun Tiak and her children can't afford regular meals. Sweet potato, root stock, corn and vegetables are their daily meal and even this kind of food they don't have often enough. They enjoy delicious food like rice and meat only at Christmas time or when there is a wedding ceremony in their village. In the evening they mostly eat boiled rice that is disproportionately mixed with large amounts of water and vegetables. Many times they go to bed without an evening meal. The money the mother earns is used for the most essential needs such as rice, salt, soap, and medication. They depend on gifts donated by richer villagers and neighbours because they cannot afford clothing.

The question is who is to blame for Ngun Tiak's worsening life? Before her husband died, their life was the same as those of the other villagers. Then the military commanded her husband to carry rations and ammunition throughout their operation in the jungle. It is not known whether he was shot dead or died of disease. Ngun Tiak tells me that if the military used him as a porter for their operations, then they should give compensation to his family. The way the armed forces treats civilians is inhuman, she says, and it has left her family in poverty.

SHORTLIST – ADULT

Silvia Patru

Targoviste, Romania

THE FUTURE OF A CHILD BORN TODAY IN THE DEVELOPING WORLD

I have been stationed in Afghanistan for six months now and from the first moment I stepped off the plane it dawned on me that what you see in American war movies is an exact replica of reality. But unlike home cinema, here you have no remote control to turn off what you see if you don't like the story line; everything is as real as it gets.

My mission here as a journalist was to objectively evaluate the situation of the Afghan children to see how they live, how they adapt to the daily inferno and what their perspectives are. Thus, I have been trying to imagine the future of a child born today in this developing country. The word 'future' may be a bit meaningless in this context, considering the fact that some of the children don't even reach the age of five, due to causes that pose no problem in developed countries (like chronic malnutrition). The deteriorating security situation and the failure of the international community to stabilize the political and social environment are risk factors for any attempt to bring up children according to the norms established in peaceful countries.

First of all, a child born today in Afghanistan would spend his/her first seconds of life in war and poverty; later on, he/she may be used by insurgents for military purposes, moreover, the drought that has been plaguing the country for the last few years and which lead to extreme hunger is an ever-present threat. The Afghan children are at a permanent risk of hunger, malnutrition and vitamin deficiencies; a great percentage of children under age five suffer from chronic malnutrition. Moreover, diseases which are easily treatable in developed countries and the lack of medicines have raised the rate of child mortality to an alarming level. What's in store for a child who does not even get basic food and treatment in order to become an adult?

If Afghan children do grow to reach the age when they should start going to school, most of them will not have access to education. A great percentage of children are not enrolled in school, due to poverty, the destruction of school buildings, the lack of teaching staff and other reasons. Children usually have to work from a young age to support their families; many work or beg on the streets of Kabul. With little to no education, Afghan children are bereft of the chance to a better life and become trapped in the maze of their hopeless situation.

The land mines are also a big issue: there are millions of them and children are vulnerable because they may mistake them for other objects and may try to pick them up, or they may just step on them while performing daily tasks, like taking care of the animals, gathering wood, tending to their family's needs etc.

One of the most important implications of the war is the fact that children live every day being afraid of death. They have suffered a great deal from displacement, poverty, instability; they are deprived of their basic rights and are subject to various forms of violence. In order to develop into normal, healthy adults, they need to live in a psychological climate of hope, safety, kindness and stability. Thus, the future of a child born today in Afghanistan would be bleak: assuming that he/she survives the poverty and lack of food and treatment and becomes an adult, he/she still has to fight to get an education, to get a job, to support the family and to stay safe from the effects of the war; even crossing the street would be a monumental task in some parts of the country, because of the landmines and the bullets. And perhaps one day, that child will be able to leave the country and head somewhere where a brighter future can be expected.

I have presented the premises for the bleak future of a child born today in Afghanistan, under the present conditions and without any further help from the international community, assuming that the child lives above the age of five, is not underweight or vitamin deficient, is psychologically resilient to the excruciating pain of displacement and war, is not killed or injured in the conflict or by natural disasters or stray landmines. Such a child would have no chance of development of any kind: his health would be weak, his education next to nonexistent, which would lead to a lack of working skills, the impossibility to get a good job and to support himself and his family, he would need constant psychological treatment, he would start a family from an early age and he would not be able to support it, living in poverty for the rest of his life, he would have virtually no access to medical care.

So Afghanistan is, without the shadow of a doubt, one of the most dangerous places to be born in. It is up to the international community to strive to make it an inhabitable place, fit for children. There are international organizations that have been working to improve the children's quality of life. If many such organizations and institutions conjugate their efforts they may actually make a difference. They can establish programs to improve sanitation, medication, education, food supply, to create an environment in which the children adapt easier. Ensuring a climate of stability and continued humanitarian assistance are of the utmost importance. Moreover, through grants, the World Bank is also helping improve the quality of life here, by improving health services and education, rural development, by financing infrastructure and fighting against climate change.

Therefore, in order to create a better life for Afghan children, the international community together with the country's government must work together and strive to create a more peaceful world.

SHORTLIST – ADULT

Dennis Penu
Greater Accra, Ghana

LIVING ON LESS THAN $2 A DAY IN THE DEVELOPING WORLD

If the leaders of our world ever wondered how the semantics of world economic indicators affected their citizens; if ever they wanted some food for thought, then they should read this story, a story of how the life of a young African girl was turned into a life of uncertainty.

Early in the morning Amerley's compound is busy with activity. Most mornings are like this with brooms kissing the floor, cocks crowing songs of freedom from their coops and the clanging sounds from the dishes being done by Mum.

Ama has been a vibrant school child for the past 5 years and a promising pupil at that. She is living in a small township with her mum and dad. Even though they (her parents) never had any education of their own, they were determined to school their only daughter; their only hope for a better future.

But that was soon to be shattered. Ama vividly remembers the events as she sat on her mat lazily but rather sombrely with a heavy heart and a heavy question, 'Why?'

Mr. Otoo, Ama's father, also recounts the day:

He was getting ready for work as a porter at the main shop in the township. Nothing was ominous about the morning's preparations. He valued his job very much; securing it after all other facilities had turned him down.

That fateful morning he had called Ama and given her 1 cedi and said: 'Be hopeful my dear daughter. Someday I will be paid higher wages and you'll get more than a cedi.'

'Thank you Daddy,' Ama had said, with genuine appreciation for this routine gesture as she hurried out of the compound for school.

'Remember to take your studies seriously and to stay out of trouble,' her mum admonished; but the words were drowned by the 10-year-old's thoughts of joy at school. Meanwhile, trouble was lurking to show up during school and she least expected that the day was going to turn sour.

It's important to reveal here that these harmonious events occurred just at the time the media was hijacked by stories about the economic downturn. The West seemed to be on fire, but the people at the grassroots in Ama's country, a developing country, in the south, seemed unaware of the repercussions of such developments.

Ama's father continues the recall of the unbelievable turn of events on the day: 'It has become difficult for us to continue paying all of you,' the shop boss announced. 'As you might have heard, the world economy has changed,' he continued. 'It's affecting our business here in this country and so we have to lay-off some workers. Mr. Kermoh, Mr. Fosu and Mr. Otoo kindly see me in my office.'

Every time else in school was serene but break time was the busiest for Ama and her schoolmates. It was the pivot of their love for school.

Ama was suffering a similar fate in school. She could no longer get a plate of food for 30 pesewas, it now costs 50 pesewas. Prices of goods had increased. The daily school fee of 50 pesewas had already siphoned half of Ama's money. She begged to get some food to eat on credit. Ama's bus fare back home could not be supported anymore by the remaining 20 pesewas. She had no option but to walk the 2-mile journey back home.

By now, Mr. Otoo had lost his job and lamentations overflowed at his house. It was clear now that it was impossible to continue seeing Ama through school. This was the end of the road.

During this interview, laced with emotions, Ama couldn't help asking: Why? Where are those invisible factors that control the world 'ecanemy'? No 'ecominy'? No, economy? Whoever controls them? If only they knew my plight. 'Oh why?' she asked, as she recounts the thoughts that came to her.

She's just 10 years old and already owed. How hopeful she was of getting the best out of education. In just 48 hours, her hopes have been shattered and her concerns have multiplied.

Life was going to drastically turn round after this episode. And sure it did. Poor Ama began to engage in menial jobs to support the family.

The quarry was close by and the stones therein became her friends. Cracking 20 buckets-full a day will be able to support her part of the family budget. At times when the quarry was closed, selling on the streets was an alternative; selling water to the road-side vendors who were too lazy to go search for water.

She'd been transformed into a 'woman' with partial economic responsibility for her family. As if that wasn't enough, Ama began avoiding her colleagues at school and the teachers. It was clear to her that everyone in class would miss her presence by virtue of her hard work and promising academic potential. The sight of school children mostly made tears run down her cheek and she dreaded it the more when she thought of the money she owed the food vendor at school.

Here in this small town, no one cared about the poor child on the streets. There were no social intervention policies to salvage her plight. The system was either a white elephant or completely non-existent.

'Wherever these invisible hands controlling my plight exist, may they hear my cry and get me back into school,' she said without knowing how, when or where this turnaround was going to take place.

SHORTLIST – ADULT

Helena Darcy
Stoneyford, Kilkenny, Ireland

LIVING ON LESS THAN $2 A DAY IN THE DEVELOPING WORLD

Eyes closed, hair filthy and stuck to his forehead, a small cockroach skitters across his face. He raises his arm to wipe it away and rolls over as much as he can until his face is pressed against his brother's back. The stench of the open sewer running past their room is overpowering, the searing heat increases as the sun powers into the sky. What more motivation does this child need to get out of his 'bed?'

This morning is the same as any other, everyone sharing the same sleeping space means they all get up together, if they're able. But they have to be able.

He and his brothers rush to the dump where a truck is driving in, dust and paper thrown up in its wake about to deposit its disgusting contents. They're small boys so they can move fast, past the mothers carrying children, past the elderly. It's a matter of survival – he who gets there first gets the spoils.

Unable to afford shoes, metal and glass split their skin, rancid earth presses into the wound and begins its work. Maybe they might find some footwear amongst this filth, maybe they will be able to get enough that they can keep the shoes. Lots of 'ifs' and 'maybes.', at least the rains are not here at the moment, with the heat and the wet, disease is rife and the boys will struggle more.

He has a cough, his chest hurts and he is scared – the cough took their mother, then their sister. Now it's just them and they have to survive. He can't wonder if the cough will take him, he has to look out for his younger brothers. He has noticed that the cough is worse now at night, it grips him right round his back. But there is no one to notice, they are invisible. Today there is food, the dogs have got to it first but they wrestle some out of their mouths. His brother finds a magazine, he rolls it up quickly and puts in inside his tee shirt. He sees a bag, he grabs it and runs, his cough makes it difficult.

Every day there is a bad man there. If he catches the children with 'things' he will snatch them off them, so they must run now; fast, pockets with some food and a bag of 'things.' They manage to find a spot where they can't be seen, there are so many people out today and until the next truck comes, they won't know if they can make any money. Sitting down, they rip open the bag to find stinking vegetables and some rotting meat even if the food is good when thrown out, the flies get in and lay their eggs. Some of the meat is alive with maggots.

They need to survive, so they eat the revolting food, maggots falling onto the ground as they cram the food into their hungry mouths … the maggots will crawl off to find the next host. His cough is very bad today, he feels weak, hot and sweating. The next truck is coming, he trips on a rock and twists his knee, he has to let his brothers go on without him as he holds his chest, grits his teeth and tries to see through his tears. The flies buzz round his head attracted to his foul breath and tears. His brothers run back, the bad man is following, they have something in their hands so he has to get up and run. Run home. Home?

Home is a room, the room is a space with a heap of rags to sleep on and tin for a roof. He lies down on the heap of rags, the pain is bad, he wraps his own arms round him, it's small comfort. He throws his head back in an attempt to draw some breath, and slowly the pain subsides and he watches his brothers.

His brothers watch him with tears in their eyes. They worry that their big brother might be taken away with the 'cough'. He sits up and smiles and they take out the magazine. They can't read but they love the pictures … and there in the middle is their hero: David Beckham. David Beckham, sitting in a beautiful place with a plate of food, his shirt is white and his hair is clean and gleaming, the boys are delighted. One day they went to the shop where the men watch television and watched through the crack in some boards. This is where they saw David Beckham playing football, he was magnificent. Today the boys found some makeup. They know they can get some money for this, it has to be taken to the lady who does the hair, she has makeup and uses it to paint the ladies faces; the ladies who go out at night like their mother used to.

He sends his brothers off. Today he just can't go with them, he feels too weak. He tells them how much to ask for and not to put it into her hand until she pays.

It's so much for one small boy to bear; he is twelve years old, very sick and 'parent' to two younger brothers. He looks after them and who knows, if the cough takes him, who will look after the young ones then? The boys come back, they're so happy, they bring him some water and an orange from the lady, they also have some money. They all lie down next to each other, they have dreams and they make plans, dreams are so important. Laughing and staring at the tin roof, they are so grateful for what they have!

He's twelve years old, he closes his eyes and drifts off to sleep. He doesn't notice the acrid smell of the sewage, he doesn't feel the flies on his eyelids … he is standing next to a table and a man in a white shirt, yes his hero.

Dreams are vital.

PASSAGES – ADULT

Maria Matthews
Kentstown, Navan, County Meath, Ireland

THE FUTURE OF A CHILD BORN TODAY IN THE DEVELOPING WORLD

... I have learnt to run fast. If I hear the sound of a gunshot I have a readymade place to hide. There I will be safe. No one will dare follow me into the minefield. I know it too well. I hate it. It has taken my brother and his best friend. So I will use it. My father left the village in search of work and never returned. My mother's distress did not last long as she became ill and died quickly. My older sister was looking after me. She died when she was thirteen. She was very beautiful and funny. She had no problem getting money to feed us. She slept during the morning and each evening would go to work in the town. But then she became sick. Now I am alone. I am not beautiful. But I will survive. Today, I beg, I go through trash cans and forage for food. To survive another year I will do what I can and use what I have, my body. But a year is a long time away. I look to the future as in a day at a time.

These are the words I imagine a child in Chad or Botswana is saying over and over again. The sad fact is though many of us are aware of it we are not physically and constantly aware so we donate a euro or two and our attention wanders to more personal details. We owe them a little more time and attention, these five million who whose lives will not linger long enough to enjoy the beautiful wonders of this world. When I use the term beautiful wonders of this world, I am talking about necessities such as clean water and electricity, a safe room where they can lie down and sleep, a safe future that will enable them to live beyond the age of fourteen in a world where Aids is not a constant humming net in the background.

Farnaz Imani Hossein Abad
Adult High School, Ottawa, Canada

LIVING ON THE LESS THAN $2 A DAY IN THE DEVELOPING WORLD

... Mani can't sleep at night, even when he is exhausted. He thinks about the rent and the face of the owner, a greedy man who just cares about money. The owner of the house warns him if he doesn't pay his rent, he will be evicted. Where can he go, with no money, three children and a sick woman in this noisy city? He looks at his sleeping children and he is afraid for their future.

He gets up and looks at his watch. The time is 5:00 am and he didn't sleep at all. He goes to the kitchen, eats a piece of bread with margarine and leaves without making a noise. He walks to his workplace. He sells socks on a busy street. He knows people don't like to buy socks from street peddlers, but this is the only source of income for his family. He buys a batch of socks for 5.000 tumans ($5) from the market and sells them for 1.000 tumans ($10).

Mani lives in hope that a few of the thousands of people that pass by everyday will stop to buy socks from him. As he works, he sees people from different classes of society. He recognizes them by their clothes and their behaviour, but this is not something that really hurts him. When he sees children go to school, though, it makes him feel guilty and depressed. He feels that he is a bad father. He doesn't know how to explain to his children that when they grow up, they will be working next to him selling socks or flowers in the street.

It is now 9:00 am and Mani has sold two pairs of socks for 25 cents each, so he has 50 cents. This means that he can't eat lunch today. He knows his wife will cook a thin soup for the children. When they buy meat, his wife cuts it into small pieces. When she finishes making soup, she takes the meat out to use it again in the next soup. This means the children get just the taste of the meat, but not the meat itself.

The meat lasts almost a month this way.

Eric Mbotiji

Bamenda, Cameroon

THE FUTURE OF A CHILD BORN TODAY IN THE DEVELOPING WORLD

... This is what goes on in most developing countries, thereby making the future of young people very uncertain. In most communities in the developing world, especially in rural areas, low levels of income do not permit parents to send their children to school. In most of these localities, hygienic conditions are deplorable. There are few hospitals and limited medical personnel, and sometimes shortages of drugs and lack of medical equipment, coupled with lack of portable drinking water, contribute to reducing life expectancy. The absence of recreational facilities in most developing countries makes the environment not viable to generate inspiration which young people need to nurture big dreams. All these have given birth to an environment which is not enabling for young people to nurture their dreams and achieve them. All these hurdles really affect the life and future of young ones growing up in developing countries. The few who are employed don't really like it where they work at the moment, but have no choice because they have to do something to earn a living. This has resulted to incompetence in many fields of work, due to lack of motivation and job satisfaction. Thus the future of a child born in the developing world is not very promising as compared to those in the developed nations.

Carlos Alberto Rosales Purizaca
Lima, Peru

LIVING ON LESS THAN $2 A DAY IN THE DEVELOPING WORLD

... Tomorrow is another day when he has to find something of value from landfills, a day when the candies are the only passport to prosperity and when the night will see the school as the depository of their only hope for something better.

There are millions of children worldwide who live as Gabriel. Who spend their days wielding illusions do not know if one day become reality. Children who are deprived of the legitimate right to a dignified life to discover in the game a vehicle for social, emotional and psychological, and from an early age are forced to work in inhumane conditions.

These children are entitled to a better future. Therefore, the best legacy we can leave these children is to build a fairer world where they have the right to good nutrition and quality education.

... If we asked Gabriel: What do you want to be when you grow up? He would say, 'I want to be Secretary General of the United Nations to ensure that all children born in a country in Africa or Latin America are not doomed to live under the dictatorship of misery.'

Gabriel's request echoes in all corners of the world's poor, because as he,·every day children are born after a few minutes of birth, die from extreme poverty. Therefore, children born in developing countries are entitled to recognition as such. The current generations of children today are educated in classrooms or living on the streets must inherit a society that respects their dignity.

Public officials, parents, politicians, educators, journalists, opinion leaders, entrepreneurs and citizens have a duty to transmit values and be an example for the generation that is growing rapidly today and tomorrow will take the reins of our society. Projects must capture the sustained growth of our children and promote initiatives to ensure their full development as individuals. The best way to express love is to ensure a world that decreases the levels of work and child malnutrition.

The dream of building such a society is unavailable, depends on our ability to engage with the future of children. They are not anonymous beings who are scattered in the streets begging for alms or selling candy. These are people who deserve the right to become players in the future and social change.

Arely Miranda González

Beijing, China

LESSONS FROM THE DEVELOPING WORLD

... *Chūn Jié* or Spring Festival in China is known in many countries as the Chinese New Year, based on the Lunar New Year celebration, during which impressive fireworks make international headlines. However, in China *Chūn Jié* is, in essence, a time for family reunion in which Chinese from all over the nation cue up for days (literally!) in order to get a train ticket and be close to their loved ones. During that week nothing else matters than reuniting with your family and sharing an endless meal, and even the hours of preparation for it!

This is why I was honored to be invited to Mrs. Jia's New Year dinner. We chatted, mainly about food, and although I had innumerable questions to ask, I decided to watch instead. In China the best way to understand culture is by becoming a simple spectator and not interfering with the way of things.

One of the most important lessons I have learned from China is that the family is an institution that deserves respect, for what it means and for what it gives to people. In developing countries like China families strengthen values of respect for elders, mutual respect, tolerance and support to others. Each person in the family plays a role in a machine that otherwise runs by itself.

Grandparents offer their advice to their children (both son or daughter and in-law) and help by taking care of the grandchild. Their children are the bread-winners who also make sure that their parents will not suffer from the questionable pension system in China. The grandchild does not know this, but he or she will become the center of the family and will reflect all the success that his or her elders could not achieve ...

List of Schools and College Entries to the Concern Worldwide 2011 Writing Competition

School	Town	County/ Province	Country
Abbey Vocational School	Donegal Town	Co. Donegal	Ireland
Adult High School	Ottawa	Ontario	Canada
Aitchison College	Lahore		Pakistan
American Heritage	Parkland	Florida	USA
American University in Central Asia	Bishek		Kyrgyzstan
Ard Scoil na nDeise	Dungarvan	Co. Waterford	Ireland
Ard Scoil Ris	Griffith Avenue	Dublin 3	Ireland
Ardgiallan Community College	Balbriggan	Co. Dublin	Ireland
Athlone Community College	Athlone	Co. Westmeath	Ireland
Australian National University	Canberra		Australia
Bahria University Islamabad	Islamabad		Pakistan
Ballinrobe Community School	Ballinrobe	Co. Mayo	Ireland
Ballinteer community school	Ballinteer	Dublin	Ireland
Banagher College	Banagher	Co. Offaly	Ireland

Bantry Youthreach	Bantry	Co. Cork	Ireland
Belfast Leersentrum	Belfast	Zoekop	South Africa
Bellows Falls Union High School	Bellows Falls	Vermont	USA
Belvedere College S.J	Great Denmark St.	Dublin 1	Ireland
Bigard Memorial Seminary	Enugu	Owerri	Nigeria
Blekinge Institute of Technology	Karlskrona	Blekinge	Sweden
Bromsgrove Senior School	Barnt Green	Worcestershire	England
Bunscoil Loreto	Gorey	Wexford	Ireland
C.B.S Charleville	Charleville	Co. Cork	Ireland
C.B.S. The Green	Tralee	Kerry	Ireland
Castletroy College	Milford	Co. Donegal	Ireland
Catholic University of Leuven	Leuven		Belgium
Christ King Girls Secondary School	Innishannon	Co. Cork	Ireland
Christian Brothers Grammar School	Omagh	Co. Tyrone	N. Ireland
Clifden Community School	Clifden	Co.Galway	Ireland
Clonburris N.S	Clondalkin	Dublin 22	Ireland
Coaiste de hÍde	Tamhlacht	Bhaile Atha Cliath	Ireland
Coláiste Chroí Mhuire	An Spidéal	Co. Galway	Ireland
Colaiste Ide	Dingle	Co. Kerry	Ireland
Coláiste Mhuire	Johnstown	Co. Kilkenny	Ireland
Coláiste Phobal Ros Cré	Roscrea	Co. Tipperary	Ireland
Coll. of Bus. Mgmt	Karachi		Pakistan

Convent of Mercy	Tuam	Co. Galway	Ireland
David W. Butler High School	Matthews	North Carolina	USA
Delphi Community Middle School	Bringhurst	Indiana	USA
Dominican College	Wicklow Town	Co. Wicklow	Ireland
Dominican College	Galway	Co. Galway	Ireland
Donabate Community College	Donabate	Co. Dublin	Ireland
Drimnagh Castle C.B.S	Walkinstown	Dublin 12	Ireland
Dublin City University	Griffith Avenue	Dublin	Ireland
Dublin Institute of Technology	Kevin Street	Dublin 8	Ireland
Dublin Institute of Technology	Aungier Street	Dublin 2	Ireland
Dun Laoghaire College of Further Education	Dun Laoghaire	Co. Dublin	Ireland
East Central University	Ada	Oklahoma	USA
English International School of Padova	Padova		Italy
Finn Valley College	Stranorlar	Co. Donegal	Ireland
Foreign Trade University	Ha Noi		Vietnam
Gaelcholaiste Luimnigh	Limerick	Co. Limerick	Ireland
Gairmscoil Einne	Aran Islands	Co. Galway	Ireland
Glenlola Collegiate School	Bangor	Co. Down	N. Ireland
Gorey Community School	Gorey	Co.Wexford	Ireland
Holy Faith Convent	Clontarf	Dublin	Ireland

Holy Family Secondary School	Newbridge	Co. Kildare	Ireland
Holy Trinity College	Cookstown	Co. Tyrone	N. Ireland
Homeschool	Eubank	California	USA
Homeschool	Newberg	Oregon	USA
Homeschooled/Crossroa ds Christian Academy	Corona	California	USA
International University of Ataturk-alatoo	Bishek		Kyrgyzstan
John the Baptist Community School	Hospital	Co Limerick	Ireland
Johnson County Community College	Olathe	Kansas	USA
Kalamalka Secondary School	Coldstream	British Colombia	Canada
Kilkenny College	Kilkenny	Co. Kilkenny	Ireland
King's Hospital	Palmerstown	Co. Dublin	Ireland
Lanesboro Community College	Lanesboro	Co. Longford	Ireland
Largy Collage	Clones	Co.Monaghan	Ireland
Laurel Hill Colaiste	Limerick	Co. Limerick	Ireland
Leawood Middle	Leawood	Kansas	USA
Lenin #1 School			Kyrgyzstan
Loreto Abbey Secondary School	Dalkey	Co. Dublin	Ireland
Loreto College Balbriggan	Balbriggan	Co. Dublin	Ireland
Loreto Community School	Milford	Co. Donegal	Ireland
Loreto secondary school	Clonmel	Co. Tipperary	Ireland
Loreto Secondary School	Wexford	Co.Wexford	Ireland
Loreto Secondary School	Fermoy	Co. Cork	Ireland

Maharaja Sawai Man Singh Vidyalaya	Jaipur		India
Maryfield College	Drumcondra	Dublin 9	Ireland
Mean Scoil Nua An Leith Triuigh	Castlegregory	Co. Kerry	Ireland
Mehmedalija Mak Dizdar	Sarajevo		Bosnia Her-zevogina
Mercy College	Sligo	Co. Sligo	Ireland
Mercy Convent	Tuam	Co. Galway	Ireland
Mercy Secondary School	Inchicore	Dublin	Ireland
Millstreet Community School	Millstreet Town	Co. Cork	Ireland
Moyle Park College	Clondalkin	Dublin 24	Ireland
National Law University	Orissa		India
National University	LaJolla	California	USA
National University of Ireland Maynooth	Maynooth	Co. Kildare	Ireland
Nazareth Area High School	Nazareth	Pennsylvannia	USA
Netaji Subhas Institute Of Technology	Dwarka	New Delhi	India
Northview High	Johns Creek	Georgia	USA
NorthWalsham High School	North Walsham	Norfolk	United Kingdom
NUI Maynooth	Maynooth	Co. Kildare	Ireland
Obafemi Awolowo University	Osun State		Nigeria
Oriel High School	Crawley	West Sussex	United Kingdom
Our Lady's Grammar School	Newry	Co. Down	N. Ireland

Petro Mohyla Black Sea State University	Mykolayiv		Ukraine
Pipers Hill College	Naas	Co. Kildare	Ireland
Pobal Scoil Caorca Dhuibhne	Dingle	Co.Kerry.	Ireland
Presentation College	Athenry	Co.Galway	Ireland
Presentation de la Salle College	Bagenalstown	Co. Carlow	Ireland
Presentation Secondary School	Clonmel	Co. Tipperary	Ireland
Presentation Secondary School	Ballyphehane	Co. Cork	Ireland
Przhevalsky #2	Karakol		Kyrgyzstan
Pukyong National University	Busan		South Korea
Ramsey Grammar School	Ramsey	Isle of Man	United Kingdom
Richard Montgomery High School	Germantown	Maryland	USA
Riverside School	Santry	Dublin	Ireland
RN Shetty Institute of Technology	Bengaluru	Bangalore	India
Rostraver Middle School	West Newton	Pennsylvannia	USA
Rush National School	Rush	Co. Dublin	Ireland
SABA-Bitola	Solunska	Macedonia	Macedonia
Sacred Heart Grammer School	Newry	Co. Armagh	N. Ireland
Sacred Heart School	Drogheda	Co. Louth	Ireland
Sacred Heart Secondary School	Clonakilty	Co. Cork	Ireland
Salendine Nook High School	Huddersfield	West Yorkshire	United Kingdom

Salerno Secondary School	Salthill	Galway	Ireland
Salesian Scondary School	Limerick	Co. Limerick	Ireland
School-Gymnazium #11	Karakol		Kyrgyzstan
Scoil Bhríde, Mercy Secondary School	Tuam	Co. Galway	Ireland
Scoil Chonglais	Baltinglass	Co. Wicklow	Ireland
Scoil Mhuire	Ennistymon	Co. Clare	Ireland
Scoil Mhuire gan Smál	Blarney	Co. Cork	Ireland
Scoil Naomh Muire	Donore	Co. Meath	Ireland
Senior High School Exelent Number 3 Kayuagung	Kayuagung	Ogan llir Regency	Indonesia
Shue-Medill Middle School	Newark	New Jersey	USA
Singapore American School			Singapore
SMA NEGERI 1 KRIAN (State Senior High School 1 Krian)	Sidoarjo	Jawa Timur	Indonesia
SMA Negeri 3	Malang	Jawa Timur	Indonesia
South East Europian University	Tetovo		Macedonia
St Andrews Junior College			Singapore
St Brigid's Convent of Mercy	Tuam	Co. Galway	Ireland
St Ciaran's College	Ballygawley	Co. Tyrone	N. Ireland
St David's Secondary School	Greystones	Co. Wicklow	Ireland
St Dominic's Secondary School	Ballyfermot	Dublin 10	Ireland

St Eunan's College	Letterkenny	Co. Donegal	Ireland
St Jean Baptiste High School	New York	New York	USA
St Joseph Of Cluny Secondary School	Killiney	Co. Dublin	Ireland
St Joseph's Academy	Kildare Town	Co Kildare	Ireland
St Joseph's Secondary School	Abbeyfeale	Co. Limerick	Ireland
St Kevin's Community College	Dunlavin	Co. Wicklow	Ireland
St Kilian's Deutsche Schule	Clonskeagh	Dublin 14	Ireland
St Killian's Vocational School	Ballinasloe	Co. Galway	Ireland
St Leo's College	Carlow	Co. Carlow	Ireland
St Macartan's College	Emyvale	Co. Monaghan	Ireland
St Mary's College	Naas	Co. Kildare	Ireland
St Mary's College	Ballysadare	Co. Sligo	Ireland
St Mary's College	Arklow	Co. Wicklow	Ireland
St Mary's High School	Midelton	Co. Cork	Ireland
St Marys Secondary School	Nenagh	Co.Tipperary	Ireland
St Mary's Secondary School	Ballina	Co. Mayo	Ireland
St Mary's Secondary School	New Ross	Co. Wexford	Ireland
St Michael's College	Ballsbridge	Dublin 4	Ireland
St Michael's College	Listowel	Co. Kerry	Ireland
St Michael's Loreto Secondary School	Navan	Co. Meath	Ireland

St Olave's Grammar School	Bromley	Kent	United Kingdom
St Patrick's Academy	Dungannon	Co. Tyrone	Ireland
St Pauls Secondary School	Oughterard	Co. Galway	Ireland
St Vincent Ferrer	New York	New York	USA
St Wolstan's Community School	Celbridge	Co. Kildare	Ireland
Stratford College	Harold's Cross	Dublin	Ireland
Sun Yat-sen University		Guangdong Province	China
Tallaght Community School	Tallaght	Dublin 24	Ireland
Texas Connections Academy at Houston	Houston	Texas	USA
The Cotswolds School	Bourton on the Water	Gloucestershire	United Kingdom
The Open University	Miton Keynes		United Kingdom
Trinity College	College Green	Dublin	Ireland
Tullamore College	Tullamore	Co. Offaly	Ireland
University College Dublin (UCD)	Belfield	Dublin 4	Ireland
University of Cape Town	Harare		Zimbabwe
University of Indonesia	Salemba	Central Jakarta	Indonesia
University of Innsbruck	Sofia		Bulgaria
University of Limerick	Limerick	Co. Limerick	Ireland
University of Nigeria	Nsukka	Enugu State	Nigeia
University of San Carlos	Cebu City		Philippines

University of Warsaw, Law School	Drzeworyt-niko		Poland
Upper Shirley High School	Shirley	Southampton	United Kingdom
Ursuline Secondary School	Thurles	Co. Tipperary	Ireland
Virginia College	Virginia	Co. Cavan	Ireland
Westport Academy of the Arts	Desert Hot Springs	California	USA
Youth Outreach Program	Nkwen Bamenda		Cameroon
Youthreach	Wicklow Town	Co. Wicklow	Ireland
Zef Lush Marku High School	Llaze Trpovski nn.	Skopje	Macedonia

Complete List of Entrants to the Concern Worldwide 2011 Writing Competition

Abdulle, Muna

Abdykalykov, Eric

Adegbemi, Bernard

Adekunle, Ola

Adeyemo, Iolade

Agamia, Hesham

Agbakwuru, Davis

Agravante, Mariecor

Ahrendt, Katie

Ajala, Basit

Akpoyeta, Ebun

Alexander, George

Alloush, Sandra

Alonge, Adrian

Al-Wadaan, Fayaz

Alymer, Christopher

Amies, Nathan

Anderson, Dominic

Anderson, Rebecca

Ansell, Ciara

Anwar, Farah

Augusto, Ashley

Austin, Kelly

Avanzo, Martina

Ayars, Emma

Bacco, Giulio

Baez, Dianna

Barrett, Niamh

Barry, Grace

Baxter, John

Bayfield, Georgina

Begley, Catherine

Beien, Carl

Bekalu, Mesfin Awoke

Beletsky, Anna

Bell, Olwyn

Bennett, Mark

Benson, Sarah

Berridjdal, Samya

Bianconi, Caolan

Bilson, James

Black, Katie

Blake, Rebecca

Bodych, Milena

Bogue, Sean

Bohan, John

Bonelli, Sonia

Bosco, Alberto

Bouanane, Selma

Boxall, Rachel

Brady, Nicola

Brady, Mary-Kate

Bravo, Catherine

Breathnach, Aodhan

Breathnach, David

Brennan, luke

Brgulja, Lejla

Briggs, Lauren

Brinn, Aisling

Broderick, Ryan

Brown, Melissa

Brown, Grace

Browne, Aislinn

Browne, Sharon

Buabeng, Adwoa

Buckley, Maire

Buckley, Orla

Bujari, Anna

Bullman, Caitlin

Burgess, Olivia

Burke, Aoife

Burke, Moira

Burke, Hazel

Burke, Louise

Burke, Rushelle

Burns, Mary

Burns, Colleen

Butler, Aisling

Butler, Lucy

Byrne, Conor

Byrne, thomas

Byrne, Caimin

Byrne, Emma

Byrne, Ashley

Caffrey, Dean

Calpin, Fintan

Campbell, Dylan

Campbell, Niamh

Canavan, James

Canavan, Maria

Carey, Sean

Carpenter, Shannon

Carr, Rory

Carr, Cassandra

Carr, Patrick

Carroll, Megan

Carroll, Anna

Carton, Helena

Casey, Darren

Casey, Nicole

Casey, Niamh

Casserly, Margaret

Cassidy, Deirdre

Cate, Karen

Caulfield, Natasha

Cawley, Clara

Chambers, Deirdre

Chew, Seng Choon

Chikumbo, Irene

Choi, Shawn

Chris, Sa Moo

Chung, Shanice

Clarke, Alice

Cleary, Ciaran

Clifford, Megan

Cody, Sophie

Cohan, Jamie

Coleman, Aoife

Collins, Lucy

Collister, Laura Beth

Concannon, Jamie

Connolly, Matthew

Connor, Cushla

Connor, Jessica

Conroy, Tadhg

Cooper, Emma

Corrigan, Oran

Corrigan, Cathal

Corrigan, Callum

Costan, Luca

Cotter, Kelly

Coyne, Angela

Cremin, Ciara

Cronin, Michael

Crowley, Claire

Cullinane, Chris

Cunningham, Darren

Cunningham, Eve

Cusack, Mairead

Cushion, Jordan

Daly, Sarah

Daneshfar, Carolina

Daniel, Ciara

Darcy, Helena

Davies, Adaoma Ejelam

Davies, Jr., Togba Rodney

Davis, Lauren

Davis, Odhran

Davis, Lucy M.

de Barra, Sinéad

Dear, Christopher

Debny, Damian

Deery, Eimear

Deery, Orla

Delargy, Shannen

Dempsey, Hannah

Depinna, Micaela

Devine, Shaun

Devine, Ciaran

Di, Julia

Dixon, Anthony

Dixon, Lauren

Dodd, Sorcha

Dolan, Adam

Donaghey, James

Donaghy, Pascal

Donnelly, Sean

Donnelly, Alanna

Donohue, Christina

Donovan, Alasdair

Dooley, Ava

Dordevic, Dani

Doughty, Paige

Dowe, Abigail

Dowling, Gerard

Doyle, Jessica

Doyle, Chelsea

Doyle, Niamh

Driver, Elizabeth

Drzezdzon, Maks

Duddy, Christopher

Duff, James

Duhig, Sophie

Dunbar, Natasha

Dunn, Fiachra

Dunne, Michelle

Dunne, kaila

Dunne, Louise

Dunne, Eimear

Durusbek , Diana

Duyile, Babatunde

Dwyer, Michael

Edgar, Armani

Elahi, Farhan

Elbert, Shannon

Elkanzi, Tasneem

Elliott, Rebecca

Ellis, Lucy

Engstrom, Isaiah

Esteves, Eden

Evans, Kristopher

Evans, Jenny

Ewulonu, Mitchell

Fagan, Lauren

Faherty, Joe

Faherty, Martin

Fahy, Niamh

Faleti, Elijah

Falvey, Lauren

Fang, Ting

Farrell, Warren

Farrell, Cora

Farrell, Nóra

Farrell, Dylan

Faulkner, Daniel

Feaheny, Jessica

Fennell, Amy

Ferguson, Leanne

Ferguson, Megan

Finn, Caroline

Finn, Amy

Finnegan, Sarah

Firman, Firmansyah Shdiiq Wardhana

Fitzgerald, Gary

Fitzgibbon, Conn

Fitzpatrick, Sadb

Fitzsimons, John

Flannery, Niamh

Flynn, Molly

Fogarty, Ruth

Foley, Sarah

Forde, Aaron

Forde, Orla

Fox, Aisling

Fox, Mark

Franchin, Sara

Franco, Ayla

Franks-Moore, Thomas

Freeman, Claire

Fuller, Ciaran

Funui, Ndifor Eleves

Furlanello, Elena

Gaffney, Ciaran

Garland, Evelyn

Gassett, Hannah

Gavrylova, Anastasia

Gaynor, James

Geoghegan, Leah

Geraghty, Jack

Germaine, Joey

Gerrard, Emer

Gichana, Edwin

Gilrane, Aoife

Goodman, Laura

Gormally, Annie

Gormley, Neassa

Gormley, Orla

Gowing, Alex

Grace, Dylan

Grant, Eimear

Grant, Rory

Grant, Kerri

Greenan, Aveen

Greene, Emma

Griffin, Dara

Grogan, Cian

Guerassimova, Lyuba

Guildea, Jamie

Guildea, Gary

Gupta, Nishant

Gurung, Asim

Haines, Georgette

Haley, Kate

Halligan, Emma

Hallhiau, Cormac

Hamill, Rían

Hamill, Céilí

Hanlon, Adam

Haque, Asif

Harding, Brian

Hardingham, Paige

Harvey, Gary

Harrington, Lauren

Harris, Jody

Harris, Ciara

Harvey, Gemma

Haughton, Amber

Hayes, Ross

Hayes, Amber

Healy, Adam

Healy, Aoife

Healy, Tara

Healy, Niamh

Heasman, Mary-Kate

Helms, Victoria (Madison)

Henderson, Niamh

Hendry, Conor

Hernon, Orna

Hickey, Ciara

Hickey, Lisa

Hicking, Ross

Higgins, Maria

Hildreth, Helen

Hogan, Jane

Hole, Cameron

Holland, Michaela

Horace, Amy

Horgan, Laura

Howard, Aoife

Hussein, Angham

Hussey, Patrick

Hyde, Aoife

Ichak, Annisa

Imani Hossein Abad, Farnaz

Irawan, Edy

Ishorari, Violet

Ivory Rogan, Nicole

Jailani, Sam

Jailani, Samia

Javed, Navish

Jefford, Charlotte

Jennings, Glenn

Johnson, Sara

Jones, Alana

Joyce, Theresa

Joyce, Roma

Kamuda, Anna

Kane, Leah

Karimi, Sami

Karimova, Diyora

Karuga, James

Kaur, Dilpreet

Kavanagh, Joseph

Keane, Elaine

Kearns, Amanda

Keating, Rebecca

Keating, Claire

Keenan, Shannon

Kekik, Mirac

Kelleher, Mark

Kelly, Charles

Kelly, Paul

Kelly, Ciaran

Kelly, Alisha

Kelly, Chloe

Kelly, Dylan

Kelly, Conor

Kelly, Rebecca

Kelly, Sean

Kelly, Joseph

Kelsey, Benjamin

Kencler, kacper

Kennedy, Niamh

Kerin, Tadgh

Kerin, Fergus

Kessler, Cristina

Khan, Ubaid

Kidd, Chloe

Kiely, Katriona

Kilderry, Kennedy

King, Paul

King, Becky

King, Rachel

King, Clara

Kinkead, Madeline

Kinsella, Ellen

Kinsella, Aoife

Kloy, Shar

Knight, Georgia

Kursite, Elga

Kuzaite, Grete

Lacey, Emma

Lam, Shirley

Langford, Jean

Larcombe, Courtney

Law, Richard

Lawani, Sonia

Lawrence, Tucker

Leahy, Katie

Lee, Aisling

Lee, Cassandra

Lee, Danielle

Lee, Gillian

Lee, Emma

Lehner, Stefanie

Lennan, James

Leonard, Matthew

Leonard, Michelle

Leonard, Amelia

Leonard Moore, Blainaid

Lian, Thang

Lian, Sian

Ligbongo, Asela

Liljequist, Alyssa

Lokko, Ethan

Lubian, Maria Elena

Lumsden, Aimeerose

Lundy, Arran

Lynch, Sophie

Lynch, Saoirse

Lynham, Darragh

lyons, ciara

Mabelson, Sarah

Macken, Ruth

Mackessy, Jade

Maguire, Stephany

Maguire, Sarah

Maguire, Ashlin

Maheshwari, Shreya

Mahon, Sarah

Mallon, Kaitlyn

Mallon, Eve

Malone, Eanna

Maloney, Joanne

Manning, Niall

Manyanga, Jimmy

Marks, Brandon

Marques, Guilherme

Martelli Agnes, Caroline

Masai, Laureen

Mason, Hannah

Matthews, Maria

Maunsell, Caroline

Mavinga, Christ

Mbotiji, Eric

Mc Avinchey, Maighread

Mc Carthy, Lauren

Mc Clay, Éilís

Mc Cool, Niamh

Mc Daid, Caolan

Mc Dermott, Cormac

Mc Dermott, Bronagh

Mc Donagh, Bernie

Mc Elwaine, Nathan

Mc Elwaine, Shay

Mc Fadden, Danny

Mc Ginley, Jordan

Mc Girr, eve

Mc Granaghan, Conor

Mc Hugh, Hannah

Mc Nally, Ciara Marie

McCann, Maeve

McCann, Conor

mccann, sean

McCarthy, Emma

McCarthy, Thomas

McCollom, Amy

McCollom, Avril

McCormick, Amanda

McDaid, Sharon

McDonagh, adam

McDonald, Sarah

McEvoy, lynsey

McGarry, Katie

McGirr, Maeve

McGirr, Rebecca

McGlinchey, Rachel

McGlynn, conor

McGrane, Jack

McGrane, Adam

McGrath, Aileen

233

McGrath, Niamh

McHugh, Michelle

Mcilvenna, Canice

McKenna, Fergal

McKeown, Ciara

McKernan, Callum

McKiernan, Ryan

McKillion, Lauren

Mcloughlin, Sean

McMahon, Helen

McMeel, Niamh

McNabb, Sarah

McNally, Sinead

McNamara, Sophie

McNelis, Catherine

McOnagle, Liam

McRedmond, Laura

McVicar, Grace

Meh, Seh

Melisbek, Aisulu

Mellon, Caitrin

Menton, Dyllon

Mhlanga, Dorothy

Mighell, Sarah

Miles, Taylor

Miller, Mark

Miranda, Arely

Moan, Sarah

Moclair, Molly

Molloy, Shane

Moloney-Quinn, James

Monds, Lydia

Moody, Karina

Moore, Justin

Moore, Catherine

Moran, Ciara

Moran, Jenny

Morgan, Evan

Morrow, Nicole

Morrow, Jodie

Morrow, Lydia

Motolo, Gudulle

Mould, Karen

Mulcahy, Rebecca

Muldoon, Molly

Mulkerrins, Gemma

Mulligan, Jude

Munroe, Hayley

Murphy, Shane

Murphy, Shane

Murphy, Ann

Murphy, Roisin

Murphy, Pamela

Murphy, Cian

Murray, Carl

Murray, James

Naughton, Beibhinn

Naveed, Ozair

Nazifi, Arta

Neachtain, Caomhán

Neary, Seán

Newton, Kiah

Nge, Nge

Nguyễn, Thanh Xuân

Nguyen thi Minh, Hanh

Ní Annlúin, Rachel

Ni Bhriain Ni Argain, Aoife

Ní Chanainn, Claire

Ní Chathail, Sarah

Ni Chleirigh, Aoife

Ní Chonceannáin, Máirín

Ní Chonchúr, Ellie

Ní Dhomhnalláin, Aoife

Ní Dhubháin, Catherine

Ní Dhúbhda, Niamh

Ní Ghoidín-Boers, Aoife

ní Leathlobhair, Lisa

Ní Lionaird, Ellen

Ni Mhaoldhomhnaigh, Aoife

Ní Mhathúna, Clodagh

Ní Nualláin, Anita

Nic Amhalghaidh, Chiomhara

Nic Gearalt, Alison

Nic Suibhne, Mollaí

Nistor, Dorin

Nix, Jack

Nolan, Shauna

Nolan, Kathy

Nolan, Hazel

Soumitra, Subinaya

Noonan, Sarah

Norris, Laura

Name, Rostamaji

Nugent, Siobhán

Nulty Grant, Erin

Ó Briain, Éamonn

O' Connor, Anthony

O' Donnell, Leonie

O' Donoghue, Aoife

O' Donovan, Ronan

Ó' Dubhshláine, Cian

O' Farrell, Paul

O' Flaherty, Seamus

O' Grady, Nicole

O' Hagan, Ellen

Ó hEochaidh, Cillín

Ó' Riain, Gearóid

O' Sullivan, Shannen

O' Sullivan, Mairead

O'Neill, Shane

O'Shea, Eric

Obioha, Uchechukwu

O'Brien, Úna

O'Brien, Michael

Obrycki, Claudia

O'Callaghan, Ashlín

Ochirbat, Amina

O'Connell, Sophia

O'Connell, James

O'Connell, Fionnuala

O'Connell, Aine

O'Connor, Ronan

O'Connor, Libby

Odai, Florent

O'Dea, Sarah

O'Dea, Sean

O'Donnell, Máire

O'Dowd, Kaitlin

O'Dowd, David

O'Driscoll, Daniel

O'Halloran, Donal

O'Hara, Craig

O'Hare, Meghan

O'Keeffe, Shauna

Olanlokun, Taofeeqat

O'Mahoney, Niamh

O'Malley, Megan
O'Neill, Amy
O'Neill, Ciara
O'Neill, Rory
O'Neill, Sean
O'Neill, Sinéad
O'Neill, Eoin
Onwubiko, Winifred
Onwumere, Odimegwu
Ord, Katie
O'Reilly, Daniel
O'Rourke, Bernard
Osborne, Elinor
O'Shea, Melissa
Osikoya, Catherine
Ostrowska, Alina
O'Sullivan, Sabhin
O'Sullivan, Jenny
O'Sullivan, Ciara
O'Sullivan-Carroll, Emma
Owens, Francesca
Owens, Laura
Owusu, Melissa
Oyediran, Mary
Oyediran, Samuel
Papponetti, Valeria
Parker, Toby
Pashley, Zoe
Patru, Silvia
Patton, Jack
Pavan, Silvia
Pawelczyk, Denise
Payne, Joanne
Pelayo, Ace

Penrose, Jess
Penu, Dennis
Permatasari, Meirna Puspita
Petlerkwong, Thitapa
Philbin, Alexandra
Plenderleith, Kim
Poliakowski, Kacper
Polion, Aoife
Porter, Olivia
Power, Fionnuala
Preddy, Krishan
Pretorius, Leone
Protacio, Ghail
Purcell, Shane
Pyne, Darragh
Quinn, Gavin
Quinn, Eoin
Rafferty, Leona
Rafferty, David
Rafferty, Nikita
Rahman, Shana
Ramdani, Alinda
Rao, Rohit
Reaney, Rebecca
Redmond, John
Rehan, Muhammad
Reid, Sean
Reid, Calum
Rellis, Cliona
Reynolds, John
Rhattigan Walsh, Sophie
Ritchey, Hadiah
Ritchey, Rebecca
Rivas, Anthon Mark

Rivera, Maria Vanessa

Roban, Daniel

Roberts, Stachel

Robson, Amber

Roche, Naomi

Rosales Purizaca, Carlos
    Alberto

Ruiz, Kaitlin

Rusalieva, Aizada

Russell, O'Dowd, Dervla

Russillo, Giorgia

Rutland, Daniel

Ryan, Pádraig

Ryan, Andrew

Sanchez, Nathalyn

Sardella, Eleonora Maria

Sargent, Áine

Savickas, David

Scally, Laura

Scanlan, Ciara

Seddo, Mary

Selehedin, Sherefa

Semyachkina, Lena

Shaba, Mariam

Shalevska, Elena

Sharifi, Rahman

Shattock, Ethan

Shaw, Emily

Shaw, Rebecca

Shaw, Rebecca

Shaw, Hazel

Shaw, Brian

Sheahan, Sarah

Sheehan, Valerie

Sheridan, Hannagh

Sherry, Jennifer

Slattery, Maurice

Slemon, Katie

Sludds, Sean

Smith, Haley

Smith, Rebecca

Smith-Williams, Lucy

Smyth, Brian

Snowden, Heather

Soar, Michael

Spencer, Sophie Louise

Stacey, Cillian

Steed, Aaron

Stefani, Vittorio

Strain, Cian

Strain, Seania

Sulaimanova, Gulmira

Sweeney, Shannon

Sweetman, Stephen

Synnott, Amy

Sysak, Jolene

Talbot, kyle

Tan, Dewi

Tessaro, Marco

Tiernan, Ben

Timmins, Marina

Tiwari, Mina

Todd, Freya

Toland, Simone

Toner, Rebecca

Torsabo, David

Travers, Calin

Traynor, Paul

Trebicka, Angelika

Tripathi, Sanjana

Troxel, Aoife

Truman, Scott

Tucker, Gavin

Turdubekov, Ulukbek

Turner, Callum

Tuseo, Elena

Umeh, Queensley

Upmanyu, Aditi

Valconi, Gina

Vance, Melissa

Vaughan, Caolan

Vegera, Daniel

Veronelli, Giulia

Vorobey, Yelena

Wade, Aisling

Walsh, Emma

Walsh, Julian

Walsh, Amy

Walsh, Laura